Acknowledgements

The compilers and the Publishers wish to thank the following for permission to use copyright material:

Contemporary Books Ltd., for *Myself*, from 'Collected Verse of Edgar A. Guest', © 1934, by Edgar A. Guest.
Fontana Paperbacks, for *Me, Give up slimming, Mum* and *My Dad, Your Dad* by Kit Wright.
Aileen Fisher, for *Noses*, from 'Up the Windy Hill' by Aileen Fisher, published by Abelard Press, N.Y., 1953. Copyright renewed 1981.
David Higham Associates Limited, for *The Ugly Child* and *Friends*, from 'The Secret Brother' by Elizabeth Jennings, published by Macmillan. Also for *Colonel Fazackerley* and an extract from *Timothy Winters*, from 'Figgie Hobbin' by Charles Causley, published by Macmillan. Also for *I saw a Jolly Hunter* from 'Union Street' by Charles Causley, published by Macmillan. Also for *The Quarrel* and *The Boy*, from 'Silver Sand and Snow' by Eleanor Farjeon, published by Michael Joseph.
André Deutsch Ltd., for *I'm The Big Sleeper, Father says, My Dad's Thumb* and *I Share My Bedroom*, from 'Mind Your Own Business' by Michael Rosen. Also for *Horrible Things*, from 'Seen Grandpa Lately' by Roy Fuller.
Penguin Books Ltd., for *The Spy*, from 'Late Home' by Brian Lee (Kestrel Books 1976) p.36. Copyright © 1976 by Brian Lee. Also for *Sharon's Life* and *Denis Law*, from 'Salford Road' by Gareth Owen (Kestrel Books 1979) p.25. Copyright © 1971, 1974, 1976, 1979 by Gareth Owen. Also for *When You're a GROWN-UP* and *Rodge Said* by Michael Rosen, from 'You Tell Me' by Roger McGough and Michael Rosen (Puffin Books 1981) p.72. Michael Rosen poems copyright © Michael Rosen, 1979. This collection copyright © Penguin Books Ltd., 1979.
Archie Barrett, for *My Shadow* and *My Picture*.
Faber and Faber Ltd., for *Folks, My Father* and *My Uncle Dan*, from 'Meet My Folks' by Ted Hughes.
The Hamlyn Publishing Group Limited, for *Hurry Home* by Leonard Clark, from 'Here and There'.
James Kirkup, for *Washing Day* by D.H. Thomas, from 'Shepherding Winds' by James Kirkup, published by Blackie & Son Ltd.
Sally Flood, for *A Working Mum*.
William Blackwood & Sons Ltd. on behalf of the Alfred Noyes Estate, for *Daddy Fell into the Pond* by Alfred Noyes.
Michael Ashworth, for *My Room*.
Spike Milligan, for *My Sister Laura*.
Julie Andrews, Hamstead Junior School (Sandwell), for *That's Me*.
John L. Foster, for *My Gramp* and *Elastic Jones* by Derek Stuart, from 'A Second Poetry Book' (Oxford University Press), compiled by John L. Foster.
Granada Publishing Ltd., for *Neighbours*, from 'Daybreak' by Leonard Clark.
Leon Rosselson for *Boys will be boys*.
Routledge & Kegan Paul PLC, for *Boys* by S. Robinson, from 'Poems by Children', edited by Michael Baldwin.
Marchette Chute, for *Jemima Jane*, from 'Around and About' by Marchette Chute. Copyright 1957, E.P. Dutton.
Michael Dugan, for *Ella McStumping* and *Herbaceous Plodd*, from 'My old dad and other funny things like him' by Michael Dugan, Longman-Cheshire, Melbourne, 1976.
Jennifer Curry, for *What Would You Like To Be When You Grow Up, Little Girl?* by Jenny Craig.
Gareth Owen, for *Growing Up*.
Stanley Cook, for *The School*, from 'Come Along', published by the author, 600 Barnsley Road, Sheffield, S5 6UA. Also for *In the Playground, Mr. Fitzsimmons, The Fire Station*, and *Action Man*, from 'Word Houses', also published by the author.
Stainer & Bell Ltd., for *Impressions of a New Boy* by Marian Collihole, from 'Themework'.
Jonathan Cape Ltd., for *First Day at School* and *He who owns the whistle rules the world* by Roger McGough, from 'In the Glassroom'.
Mrs. A.M. Walsh, for *Bus to School*, from 'Roundabout by the Sea' (OUP) by John Walsh. Also for *Joan Who Hates Parties*, from 'The Truants' (Heinemann), by John Walsh.
Jane Whittle, for *The Lollipop Lady*.
Oxford University Press, for *Out of School*, from 'Tomorrow is My Love' by Hal Summers.
Macmillan, London and Basingstoke, for *Parents' Evening* by Shirley Toulson, from 'Allsorts 4'.
Christine Forster, for *Window Cleaning*.
Gregory Harrison, for an extract from *The Dustbin Men*, copyright ©, from 'The Night of the Wild Horses', published by Oxford University Press.
The Literary Trustees of Walter de la Mare and The Society of Authors as their representative, for *Sooeep* by Walter de la Mare.
Angus & Robertson (U.K.) Ltd., for *The Barber* and *The Porter*, from 'A Book of Kids' by C.J. Dennis. Also for *Walter Spaggot*, from 'The Ombley-Gombley' by Peter Wesley-Smith.
World's Work Ltd., for *The Cobbler, The Florist* and *Sandwich Men* by Rachel Field, from 'Poems for Children', selected from 'Taxis,and Toadstools'. Copyright © 1926 by Doubleday & Co. Inc. Copyright © 1924 by Yale Publishing Company. Copyright © 1926 by Crowell Publishing Company. First published in Great Britain 1962. All rights reserved.
Jean Kenward, for *The Dressmaker* and *Listen, I'll Tell You*.
J.M. Dent & Sons Ltd., for *Dan the Watchman*, from 'Stirabout Lane' by John D. Sheridan.
Harper & Row, Publishers, Inc., for *Engineers*, from 'Puddin' an' Pie' by Jimmy Garthwaite. Copyright, 1929, by Harper & Row, Publishers, Inc. Renewed 1957, by Merle Garthwaite.
Harcourt Brace Jovanovich, Inc., for *Manual System*, from 'Smoke and Steel' by Carl Sandburg, copyright 1920

Acknowledgements

by Harcourt Brace Jovanovich, Inc., copyright 1948 by Carl Sandburg.
The Acorn Press, for *The Squirrel* by Sylvia Read.
Brian Lee, for *Toffee-Slab.*
Collins Publishers, for *I'm so mad I could scream!,* from 'I'm Mad at You' by William Cole, published by Collins © William Cole 1978.
Arnold Spilka, for *A Little Girl I Hate,* from 'A Rumbudgin of Nonsense' by Arnold Spilka.
Basil Blackwell Publisher Ltd., for *Sir Nicketty Nox* by Hugh Chesterman.
Penelope Rieu, for *Sir Smasham Uppe* by E. V. Rieu.
Methuen Children's Books, for *Bad Sir Brian Botany,* from 'When We Were Very Young' by A. A. Milne.
Russel & Volkening, Inc., as agents for the author, for *The Folk Who Live in Backward Town* by Mary Ann Hoberman. Copyright © 1959, by Mary Ann Hoberman.
David Higham Associates Limited, for *Aunt Kate: a moral story* by Shirley Toulson from, 'Allsorts 4'.
Curtis Brown Ltd., for *When I Grow Up* by William Wise. Copyright © 1956 by William Wise.

We have been unable to trace the copyright owners of the following poems and should be pleased to hear from them or their heirs and assigns. In the meantime we venture to include:

Sing a Song of People by Lois Lenski; *Me* by Deepak Kalha; *The Useful Art of Knitting* by Katherine Craig; *Grandma's Knitting* by Claire Howard; *Postman's Knock* by Rodney Bennett; *Nurse* by M. Howgate; *The Fair* by E.M. Stanton; *Speedway Racing* by Ana Balduque; *What do you collect?* by Wes Magee; *Taking Medicine* by Valerie Seekings; *Table Manners* by Gelett Burgess.

Poetry Plus

Book Five

People are Strange?

Written and compiled by

B.R. Marney
M. Hussamy
A.N. Ashton
S.M. Parle

Illustrated by Peter Joyce

Schofield & Sims Ltd. Huddersfield

0 7217 0435 2

First Printed 1984
Reprinted 1985, 1987, 1990

Poetry Plus is a series of five books:

Book 1 0 7217 0431 X
Book 2 0 7217 0432 8
Book 3 0 7217 0433 6
Book 4 0 7217 0434 4
Book 5 0 7217 0435 2

Foreword

One of the aims of *Poetry Plus* is to stimulate children to write their own poems. To encourage this, each section begins with a series of thought-provoking questions and relevant vocabulary. In addition, each provides ideas for inter-related topic work which should promote higher reading skills and simple research.

Poetry Close-up pages consider individual poems and related interest areas.

The poems have been carefully selected for variety and quality and are grouped so that immediate interests and enthusiasms can be pursued.

We hope that children will enjoy reading and listening to the poems in *Poetry Plus* and that the series will encourage them to write creatively.

Typeset in England by Clare Gibbs, Pen to Print, Oxford
Printed in England by Garnett Dickinson Print Ltd, Rotherham.

Contents

Contents

Contents

Sing a Song of People

Sing a song of people
Walking fast or slow;
People in the city,
Up and down they go.

People on the sidewalk,
People on the bus;
People passing, passing,
In back and front of us.
People on the subway
Underneath the ground;
People riding taxis
Round and round and round.

People with their hats on,
Going in the doors;
People with umbrellas
When it rains and pours.
People in tall buildings
And in stores below;
Riding elevators
Up and down they go.

People walking singly,
People in a crowd;
People saying nothing,
People talking loud.
People laughing, smiling,
Grumpy people too;
People who just hurry
And never look at you!

Sing a song of people
Who like to come and go;
Sing of city people
You see but never know!

LOIS LENSKI

People are Strange?

Myself

"I have to live with myself, and so
I want to be fit for myself to know;"

Read the poems in this section and think about the following descriptions of very different children.

What kind of person are you?

.... Think of — muddy clothes .... an untidy bedroom .... sticky fingers .... lots of chatter .... arguments and squabbles .... excited screams .... climbing and chasing .... rough games .... cuts and grazes.

.... Think of — clean, tidy clothes .... well-combed hair .... good table manners .... pink knees .... quiet conversations .... well-brushed teeth .... neat exercise books.

If you wish to write your own poem, these words may help you.

friendly	sharing	pleasant	bumptious	nervous
clean	honest	brash	extrovert	smart
happy	shy	plain	dirty	helpful
anxious	ordinary	pretty	lonely	bold

Inside Myself

If you could see inside yourself you would be amazed. Your body has lots of complicated parts and many different systems to keep you alive. To help you understand how your body works, make a detailed study of one of the following:

Air and Breathing
Food and Digestion
The Heart and the Blood System
Bones and Muscles

If you wish, your study could be part of a larger project you undertake with some of your friends.

If you turn to page 16 you will find some questions on the poems themselves and some more things to do.

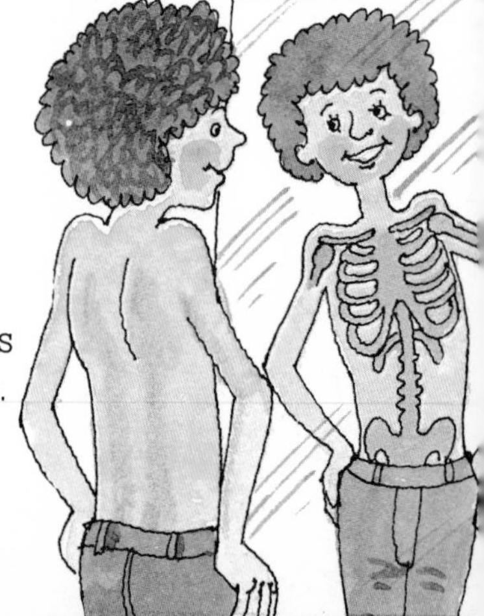

Myself

I have to live with myself, and so
I want to be fit for myself to know;
I want to be able as days go by
Always to look myself straight in the eye.
I don't want to stand with the setting sun
And hate myself for the things I've done.

EDGAR A. GUEST

Me

You got no right
to look at me,
There might be things
I don't want you to see.
Things I need
to hide
behind this mask,
my face.

DEEPAK KALHA

Me

My mum is on a diet,
My dad is on the booze,
My gran's out playing Bingo
And she was born to lose.

My brother's stripped his motor bike
Although it's bound to rain.
My sister's playing Elton John
Over and over again.

What a dim old family!
What a dreary lot!
Sometimes I think that I'm the only
Superstar they've got.

KIT WRIGHT

Noses

I looked in the mirror
and looked at my nose:
it's the funniest thing,
the way it grows
stuck right out where all of it shows
with two little holes where the breathing goes.

I looked in the mirror
and saw in there
the end of my chin
and the start of my hair
and between there isn't much space to spare
with my nose, like a handle, sticking there.

If ever you want
to giggle and shout
and can't think of what
to do it about,
just look in the mirror and then, no doubt,
you'll see how funny YOUR nose sticks out!

AILEEN FISHER

My Face

My face isn't pretty,
Nor is it quite plain —
I suppose it's an ordin'ry
Face in the main.

My mum says, 'If even
You had your hair curled,
You wouldn't exactly
Be a Miss World,

But cheer up, my lovely,
Don't look glum all the while —
You'd look so much nicer
If only you'd smile!'

ANON.

The Ugly Child

I heard them say I'm ugly.
I hoped it wasn't true.
I looked in the mirror
To get a better view,
And certainly my face seemed
Uninteresting and sad.
I *wish* that either it was good
Or else just very bad.

My eyes are green, my hair is straight,
My ears stick out, my nose
Has freckles on it all the year,
I'm skinny as a hose.
If only I could look as I
Imagine I might be.
Oh, the crowds would turn and bow.
They don't — because I'm me.

ELIZABETH JENNINGS

I'm The Big Sleeper

I'm the big sleeper
rolled up in his sheets
at the break of day

I'm a big sleeper living soft
in a hard kind of way

The light through the curtain
can't wake me
I'm under the blankets

you can't shake me
the pillow rustler
and blanket gambler
a mean tough eiderdown man

I keep my head
I stay in bed.

MICHAEL ROSEN

The Spy

Sometimes at night I crawl out of my bed,
  And tiptoe on to the landing,
Because I'm *sure* they've been talking about me,
  And how I want to know what they've said!

I crane and I stretch, then, if I can't hear
  I creep softly down to the hall,
— But mind the creaks on steps three and eleven! —
  Heart thumping, mouth dry, with something like fear.

Though it's against all the rules, I still dare
  To shuffle right up to the door,
Drawn on by murmurs I can't understand,
  The rumour of Truth in the air,

And kneel there for ages shivering with cold
  My bare feet on the bare lino,
An ear to the keyhole, holding my breath —
  What is it that makes me so bold?

Doing wrong — and the dark — the sensation
  Of finding it all out at last;
The things they don't say, the things they won't tell —
  It's all a shocking temptation:

And I'll only find out by playing this game,
  What they think of me, what I am;
Not knowing's much more than I can put up with,
  And asking them — just isn't the same.

BRIAN LEE

My Shadow

Have you ever tried
to catch the shadow
clinging to your toes?
Watch it climbing
walls and steps
all bent before your nose?

Well, I have!

Have you ever tried
to push your shadow
in a barrow full of bricks?
Rub it out?
Or pin it down
with some garden sticks?

Well, I have!

Have you ever wished
to twirl that shadow
round about your head?
Tie it up
in lumpy knots
and make it go to bed?

Well, I have!

ARCHIE BARRETT

When I Grow Up

When I grow up,
I think I'll be
A detective
With a skeleton key.

I could be a soldier
And a sailor too;
I'd like to be a keeper
At the public zoo.

I'll own a trumpet
And I'll play a tune;
I'll keep a spaceship
To explore the moon.

I'll be a cowboy
And live in the saddle;
I'll be a guide
With a canoe and a paddle.

I'd like to be the driver
On a diesel train;
And it must be fun
To run a building crane.

I'll live in a lighthouse
And guard the shore;
And I know I'll want to be
A dozen things more.

For the more a boy lives
The more a boy learns —
I think I'll be a lot of them
By taking turns.

WILLIAM WISE

Poetry Close-up

1. In the poem 'When I Grow Up' we hear about
'A detective
With a skeleton key.'
What is a skeleton key and why would a detective use it?
2. Who is the spy in the poem by Brian Lee?
On whom is he spying? Why?
3. With what object does Aileen Fisher compare her nose?
4. What is the 'Big Sleeper' dreaming about in Michael Rosen's poem?
5. Edgar Guest in his poem 'Myself' says:
"I want to be fit for myself to know".
What do you think he means?
6. If you were not yourself, who would you like to be?
Describe why you would like to be that person and
what you would do.
7. Write three different views of yourself.
a) How you see yourself;
b) How you imagine an adult might see you;
c) How you imagine someone your own age might see you.

Other Things To Do

1. Discuss with your friends what you think these proverbs mean:
Spare the rod and spoil the child.
Children should be seen and not heard.
Do you agree with them? Why?
2. Paint or draw a self-portrait. Use a mirror if you wish.
3. Do you know your birth sign? If you do, look in a paper and
find your horoscope. Do you believe it will come true?

My Family

"Other folks' folk get so well known,
But nobody knows about my own."

The writer of the above lines obviously thinks that his family is not interesting in any way. However, if you read the poems in this section and think about the following questions, then perhaps you will realise that we can find interesting things about every family.

Do these descriptions remind you of your family?

.... Think of — laughing babies .... noisy brothers
.... bossy sisters .... weary parents.

.... Think of — arguments and games .... laughter and tears ....
hobbies and interests .... holidays and outings.

Do you visit your relatives?

.... Think of — where they live .... how you get there .... your last visit .... your favourite relatives.

If you wish to write your own poem, these words may help you.

sharing	fun	jokes	play	twin	adopt
grumbles	anger	shouts	quarrels	cousin	niece
fights	stories	elderly	nephew	godson	wrinkles
kin	in-laws	caring	worry	overseas	ancestors

Famous Families

Can you draw the family tree of our Monarch?

Choose two members of the present Royal Family. Give their full official names and titles and write a few sentences about them.

What can you find out about two of these previous Kings and Queens?

King Alfred King Canute William the Conqueror Elizabeth I
Queen Victoria Richard the Lionheart King Henry VIII

If you turn to page 39 you will find some questions on the poems themselves and some more things to do.

Folks

I've heard so much
about other folks' folks,
How somebody's Uncle
told such jokes
The cat split laughing
and had to be stitched,
How somebody's Aunt
got so bewitched
She fried the kettle
and washed the water
And spanked a letter
and posted her daughter.
Other folks' folk get so well known,
But nobody knows about my own.

TED HUGHES

Hurry Home

You had better hurry home for your supper's nearly ready,
Your mother's in the kitchen and she's awfully wild,
She's been shouting at the cat, and she keeps on saying,
"O where has he got to, the wretched child?"

She has been to the front door and looked through the window
And now she's banging on the frying-pan,
The plates and the dishes are all on the table,
So run, my boy, as fast as you can.

Don't you know she's cooking your favourite supper,
Potatoes in their jackets and beefsteak pie?
She's made a jug of custard for the pudding in the oven,
Get a move on, Joe, the stars are in the sky.

They've all left the factory, the streets will soon be empty,
No more playing now, it's time you fed,
It really is a shame to keep your mother waiting,
So come have your supper, and then off to bed.

LEONARD CLARK

Give up slimming, Mum

My Mum
is short
and plump
and pretty
and I wish
she'd give up
slimming.

So does Dad.

Her cooking's
delicious —
you can't
beat it —
but you really can
hardly bear
to eat it —
the way she sits
with her eyes
brimming,
watching you
polish off
the spuds
and trimmings
while she
has nothing
herself but a small
thin dry
diet biscuit;
that's all.

My Mum
is short
and plump
and pretty
and I wish
she'd give up
slimming.

So does Dad.

She says she
looks as though
someone had
sat on her —
BUT WE LIKE MUM
WITH A BIT
OF FAT ON HER!

KIT WRIGHT

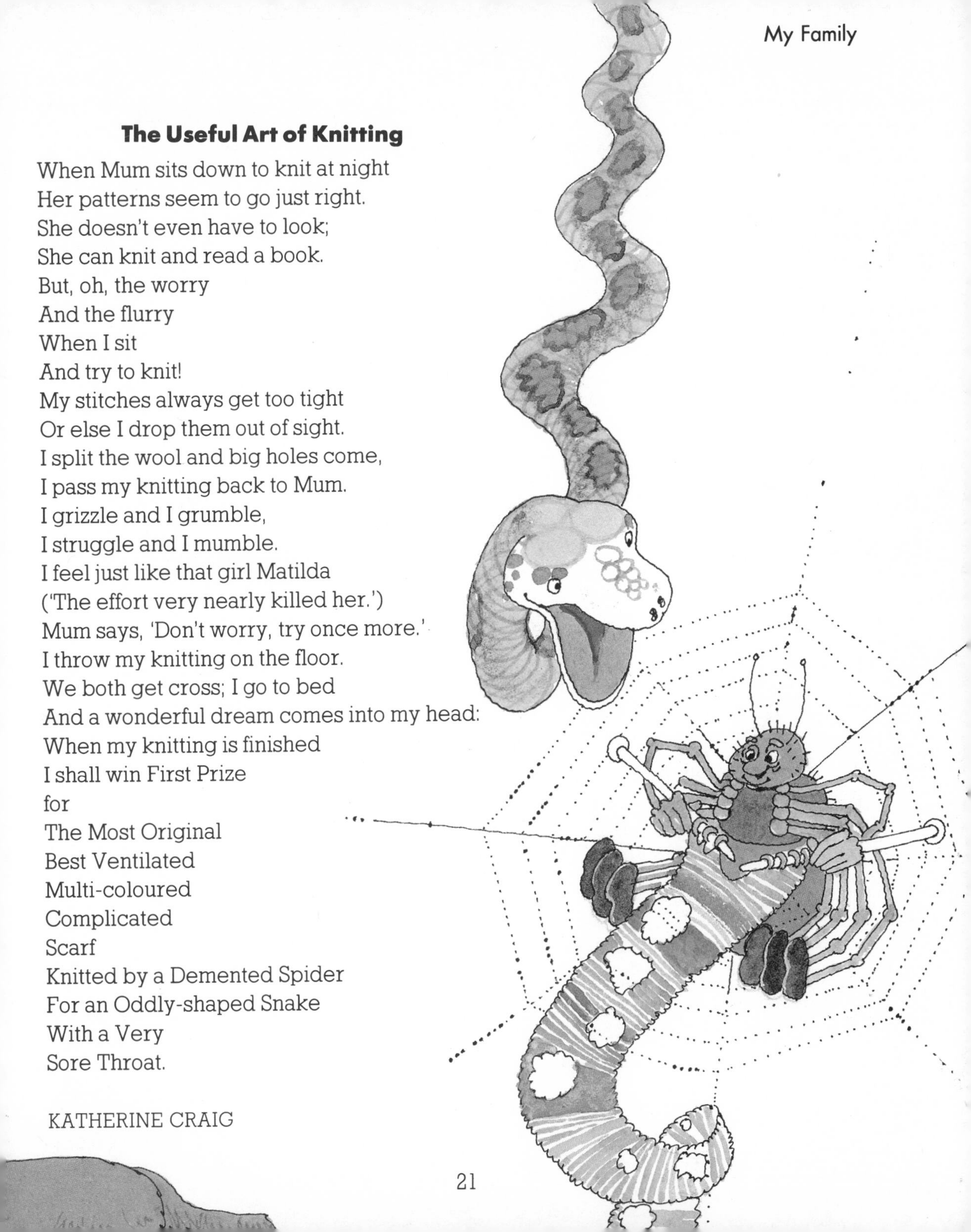

The Useful Art of Knitting

When Mum sits down to knit at night
Her patterns seem to go just right.
She doesn't even have to look;
She can knit and read a book.
But, oh, the worry
And the flurry
When I sit
And try to knit!
My stitches always get too tight
Or else I drop them out of sight.
I split the wool and big holes come,
I pass my knitting back to Mum.
I grizzle and I grumble,
I struggle and I mumble.
I feel just like that girl Matilda
('The effort very nearly killed her.')
Mum says, 'Don't worry, try once more.'
I throw my knitting on the floor.
We both get cross; I go to bed
And a wonderful dream comes into my head:
When my knitting is finished
I shall win First Prize
for
The Most Original
Best Ventilated
Multi-coloured
Complicated
Scarf
Knitted by a Demented Spider
For an Oddly-shaped Snake
With a Very
Sore Throat.

KATHERINE CRAIG

Washing Day

The chalk-lined tub, like a coral basin, is choked with soap and water.
Clusters of still bubbles, from the bottom rise,
Exploding into steam blown eyes.
Soapy, shimmering bubbles rise, dilate and burst.
Foggy patches in the kitchen linger,
Clinging to the window with a running finger.
Steam drifts up, pricking mum's plagued cheeks,
Her coarse red hands glissade into water,
Her sore face portraying gnawing anger.
Outside, her warm wet hands and face are horse-whipped by the wind,
The billowing washing, pouches and prances,
In ghostly uniformity chaotically dances.

D.H. THOMAS

A Working Mum

From morning, till night,
Life is one maddening rush.
The alarm bell rings,
You awake to a fuss.
Jump from your bed, to fight
For a place on a bus.
Someone, who had stood
Close behind you,
Now you discover
Is in front of the queue.

You don't want trouble,
So what do you do?
You stand there fuming,
The bus draws alongside,
A quick kick on her heel,
Now you're climbing inside.
You smile at the conductor,
It's just made your day,
She's still looking around her,
While the bus draws away.

You arrive in work,
At the stroke of nine.
You clock your card,
The weather is fine.
You smile all around,
'Good Morning', to you.
Then a voice in your ear,
Bawls, 'Have you nothing to do?'
You sit down quickly,
You have laddered your tights.

Seems today you have,
Nothing but frights.
You keep your head down,
You daren't look up.
The hooter blows,
You run for a cup.
The canteen is full,
Back in the queue.
You wait so long,
The hooters just blew.

Though you feel thirsty,
You have to get back,
If you dawdle too long,
You will get the sack.
So you rush and you pant,
Till you get through the day.
There goes the hooter,
You're on your way.
You join the bus queue,
The one at the top.

The bus is full,
It won't even stop.
You are hungry and cold,
You've had a long day.
No wonder your hair,
Shows streaks of grey.
You made it at last,
There is the gate.
Time for a cuppa?
'Mum, why are you late?'

SALLY FLOOD

My Dad, Your Dad

My dad's fatter than your dad,
Yes, my dad's fatter than yours:
If he eats any more he won't fit in the house,
He'll have to live out of doors.

Yes, but my dad's balder than your dad,
My dad's balder, OK?
He's only got two hairs left on his head
And both are turning grey.

Ah, but my dad's thicker than your dad,
My dad's thicker, all right,
He has to look at his watch to see
If it's noon or the middle of the night.

Yes, but my dad's more boring than your dad.
If he ever starts counting sheep
When he can't get to sleep at night, he finds
It's the sheep that go to sleep.

But my dad doesn't mind your dad.
Mine quite likes yours too.
I suppose they don't always think much of Us!
That's true, I suppose, that's true.

KIT WRIGHT

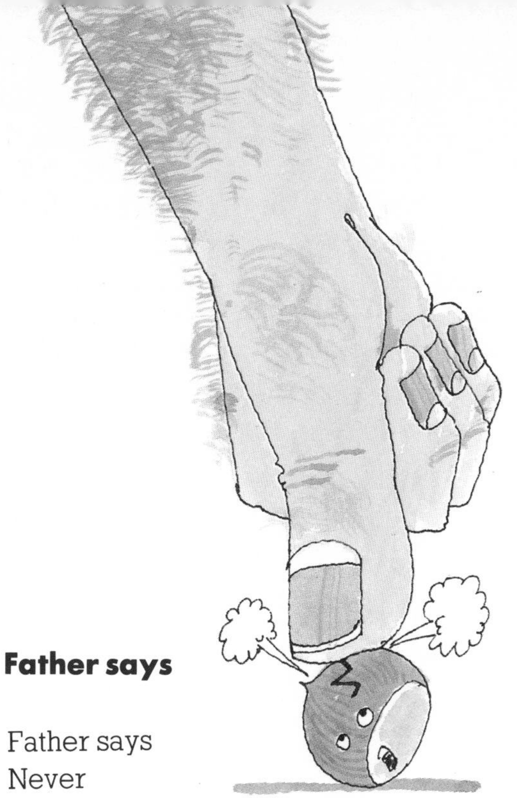

My Dad's Thumb

My dad's thumb
can stick pins in wood
without flinching —
it can crush family-size matchboxes
in one stroke
and lever off jam-jar lids without piercing
at the pierce here sign.

If it wanted
it could be a bath-plug
or a paint-scraper
a keyhole cover or a tap-tightener.

It's already a great nutcracker
and if it dressed up
it could easily pass
as a broad bean or a big toe.

In actual fact, it's quite simply
the world's fastest envelope burster.

MICHAEL ROSEN

Father says

Father says
Never
let
me
see
you
doing
that
again
father says
tell you once
tell you a thousand times
come hell or high water
his finger drills my shoulder
never let me see you doing that again.

My brother knows all his little sayings off by heart
so we practise them in bed at night.

MICHAEL ROSEN

My Father

Some fathers work at the office, others work at the store,
Some operate great cranes and build up skyscrapers galore,
Some work in canning factories counting green peas into cans,
Some drive all night in huge and thundering removal vans.

But mine has the strangest job of the lot,
My Father's the Chief Inspector of — What?
O don't tell the mice, don't tell the moles,
My Father's the Chief Inspector of HOLES.

It's work of the highest importance because you never know
What's in a hole, what fearful thing is creeping from below.
Perhaps it's a hole to the ocean and will soon gush water in tons,
Or maybe it leads to a vast cave full of gold and skeletons.

Though a hole might seem to have nothing but dirt in
Somebody's simply got to make certain.
Caves in the mountain, clefts in the wall,
My Father has to inspect them all.

That crack in the road looks harmless. My Father knows it's not.
The world may be breaking into two and starting at that spot.
Or maybe the world is a great egg, and we live on the shell,
And it's just beginning to split and hatch: you simply cannot tell.

If you see a crack, run to the phone, run!
My Father will know just what's to be done.
A rumbling hole, a silent hole,
My Father will soon have it under control.

Keeping a check on all these holes he hurries from morning to night.
There might be sounds of marching in one, or an eye shining bright.
A tentacle came groping from a hole that belonged to a mouse,
A floor collapsed and Chinamen swarmed up into the house.

A Hole's an unpredictable thing —
Nobody knows what a Hole might bring.
Caves in the mountain, clefts in the wall,
My Father has to inspect them all!

TED HUGHES

Daddy Fell into the Pond

Everyone grumbled. The sky was grey.
We had nothing to do and nothing to say.
We were nearing the end of a dismal day.
And there seemed to be nothing beyond,
 Then
  Daddy fell into the pond!

And everyone's face grew merry and bright,
And Timothy danced for sheer delight.
'Give me the camera, quick, oh quick!
He's crawling out of the duckweed!' Click!

Then the gardener suddenly slapped his knee,
And doubled up, shaking silently,
And the ducks all quacked as if they were daft,
And it sounded as if the old drake laughed.
Oh, there wasn't a thing that didn't respond
 When
  Daddy fell into the pond!

ALFRED NOYES

I Share My Bedroom

I share my bedroom with my brother
and I don't like it.
His bed's by the window
under my map of England's railways
That has a hole in just above Leicester
where Tony Sanders, he says,
killed a Roman centurion
with the Radio Times.

My bed's in the corner
and the paint on the skirting board
wrinkles when I push it with my thumb
which I do sometimes when I go to bed
sometimes when I wake up
but mostly on Sundays
when we stay in bed all morning.

That's when he makes pillow dens
under the blankets
so that only his left eye shows
and when I go deep-bed mining
for elastoplast spools
that I scatter with my feet
the night before,
and I jump on to his bed
shouting: eeyoueeyoueeyouee
heaping pillows on his head:
'Now breathe, now breathe'
and then there's quiet and silence
so I pull it away quick
and he's there laughing all over
sucking fresh air along his breathing-tube fingers.

Actually, sharing's all right.

MICHAEL ROSEN

The Quarrel

I quarrelled with my brother,
I don't know what about,
One thing led to another
And somehow we fell out.
The start of it was slight,
The end of it was strong,
He said he was right,
I knew he was wrong!

We hated one another.
The afternoon turned black.
Then suddenly my brother
Thumped me on the back,
And said, 'Oh come along
We can't go on all night —
I was in the wrong.'
So he was in the right.

ELEANOR FARJEON

The Twins

In form and feature, face and limb,
I grew so like my brother
That folks got taking me for him
And each for one another.
It puzzled all our kith and kin,
It reach'd an awful pitch;
For one of us was born a twin
And not a soul knew which.

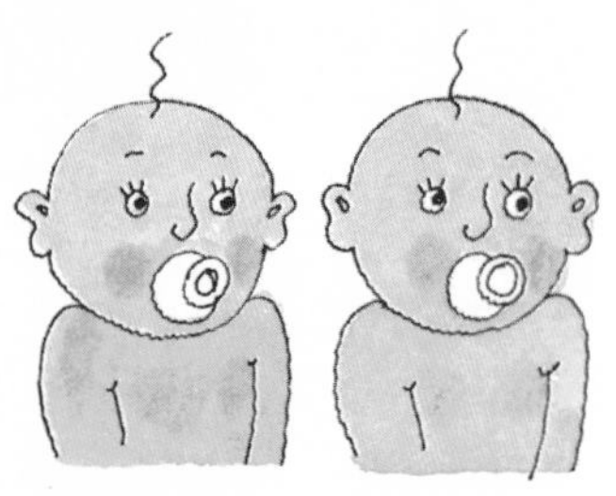

This fatal likeness even dogg'd
My footsteps when at school,
And I was always getting flogg'd —
For John turn'd out a fool.
I put this question hopelessly
To everyone I knew, —
What *would* you do, if you were me,
To prove that you were *you?*

One day (to make the matter worse),
Before our names were fix'd,
As we were being wash'd by nurse,
We got completely mix'd.
And thus, you see, by Fate's decree,
(Or rather, nurse's whim),
My brother John got christen'd *me*,
And I got christen'd *him*.

Our close resemblance turn'd the tide
Of my domestic life;
For somehow my intended bride
Became my brother's wife.
In short, year after year the same
Absurd mistakes went on;
And when I died — the neighbours came
And buried brother John!

HENRY SAMBROKE LEIGH

My Sister Laura

My sister Laura's bigger than me
And lifts me up quite easily.
I can't lift her, I've tried and tried;
She must have something heavy inside.

SPIKE MILLIGAN

My Room

I love my room
I hate anybody who goes in it.
I keep all my secrets
In my room.

My Lucy loves my room.
I hate her.
She mucks it up
And I get blamed.

My Wendy loves my room.
I definitely hate her.
She takes all my books
And I can't find one.

Am I allowed in their room?
Not likely!
Books and dolls and pillows
Come flying out at me.
I love their room.

MICHAEL ASHWORTH

That's Me

Everything that happened that morning is so clear to me,
Although it was all three months ago.
'Will you be all right mum — you don't seem well?'
'Yes, off to school like a good girl.'
But I don't understand decimals this morning.
I don't want to change my library book,
  and yet I love reading.
Must I go to the swimming-baths this afternoon?
Although I know I'm nearly ready for my green braid.
  I want to go *home*.
The four o'clock bell,
I race up the road until my breath heaves in my throat.
Near home I dawdle, linger, drag —
I can hear my own heart
  and my own footsteps.
A rush of speed up the path —
  a dash at the door —
Dad's smiling face meets me,
His laughing voice tells me I have a new brother.
'You're the eldest, you choose his name.'

The eldest! the big sister!
  That's ME.

JULIE ANDREWS

Grandfather

I remember
His sparse white hair and lean face . . .
Creased eyes that twinkled when he laughed
And the sea-worn skin
Patterned to a latticework of lines.
I remember
His blue-veined, calloused hands,
Long gnarled fingers
Stretching out towards the fire —
Three fingers missing —
Yet he was able to make model yachts
And weave baskets.
Each bronzed Autumn
He would gather berries.
Each breathing Spring
His hands were filled with flowers.
I remember
Worshipping his fisherman's yarns,
Watching his absorbed expression
As he solved the daily crossword
With the slim cigarette, hand rolled,
Placed between his lips.
I remember
The snowdrops,
The impersonal hospital bed,
The reek of antiseptic.

I remember, too,
The weeping child
And wilting daffodils
Laid upon his grave.

SUSAN HRYNKOW (aged 13)

My Gramp

My gramp has got a medal.
On the front there is a runner.
On the back it says:
Senior Boys 100 Yards
First William Green
I asked him about it,
but before he could reply
Gran said, 'Don't listen to his tales.
The only running he ever did
was after the girls.'
Gramp gave a chuckle
and went out the back
to get the tea.
As he shuffled down the passage
with his back bent,
I tried to imagine him,
legs flying, chest out,
breasting the tape.
But I couldn't.

DEREK STUART

Grandma's Knitting

My Grandma likes knitting, knitting, knitting,
Soon she'll have enough to go round the world.
Then she'll make him a hat
With a bobble on it the size of Africa.
After that she'll knit a cloak to go under the hat.
One day I'll help her knit the sunshade for the sun.
Then she'll knit more white clouds.

When I'm older I'll sew, sew, sew up all the knitting.
But still she has time to knit me a jumper.
She'll knit a rope long enough to touch heaven and hell at the same time.

But she'll find time to knit me bedsocks.
Then she'll work very hard to knit a new sandy bottom
For the sea and more liana vines for the jungle.
But I'm sure she'll have time to knit me a hat.

CLAIRE HOWARD

My Uncle Dan

My Uncle Dan's an inventor, you may think that's very fine.
You may wish he was your Uncle instead of being mine —
If he wanted he could make a watch that bounces when it drops,
He could make a helicopter out of string and bottle tops
Or any really useful thing you can't get in the shops.
But Uncle Dan has other ideas:
The bottomless glass for ginger beers,
The toothless saw that's safe for the tree,
A special word for a spelling bee
(Like Lionocerangoutangadder),
Or the roll-uppable rubber ladder,
The mystery pie that bites when it's bit —
My Uncle Dan invented it.
My Uncle Dan sits in his den inventing night and day.
His eyes peer from his hair and beard like mice from a load of hay.
And does he make the shoes that will go walks without your feet?
A shrinker to shrink instantly the elephants you meet?
A carver that just carves from the air steaks cooked and ready to eat?
No, no, he has other intentions —
Only perfectly useless inventions:
Glassless windows (they never break),
A medicine to cure the earthquake,
The unspillable screwed-down cup,
The stairs that go neither down nor up,
The door you simply paint on a wall —
Uncle Dan invented them all.

TED HUGHES

Aunt Kate: a moral story

When Aunt Kate woke each shining day
She started nagging right away.
'Shut the window,' 'Open the door,'
'Pick your pyjamas up from the floor,'
'Let the cat in,' 'Make some tea,'
'Why do you never listen to me?'
'Stop fidgeting,' 'Your tie is bent.'
She started so and on it went
From breakfast through to supper-time,
Till even breathing seemed a crime.
Her nephews and her nieces too
Were at their wits' ends what to do.

One summer-time she made a plan
To spend a week with Cousin Anne
She turned the gas off, packed her case,
Left her instructions all over the place.
She went to the station to catch her train,
And her nieces began to smile again.
Her nephews began to laugh and sing,
And they wouldn't be quiet for anything.
Meanwhile at the station, Aunt Kate found
A way to boss everyone around;
Station-master and guards and all
Were running about at her beck and call.
She complained of the service, the dirt and the crowd,
The trains were too dusty, their engines too loud.

Managers, Unions, Heads of the State
Could cope with the Press, but not with Aunt Kate.
They promised her Jaguars, planes or a bike
To arrest the threat of a General Strike.
But she being averse to both pedals and flights
Stood with her ticket demanding her rights,
Until they came up with a masterful plan
For delivering Auntie to her Cousin Anne,
'If you'll drive the train it will all be all right,
The engine so quiet not a mouse could take fright.'
So Kate drove that diesel and felt her real power,
And she sang and she whistled for one happy hour.
Her hat had blown off, and her face and her hair
Were covered in oil, but she didn't care;
And Anne when she saw her just couldn't guess
That this jolly lady, in such a great mess,
Was querulous Kate whom she'd dreaded to meet.

All you British Aunties, too painfully neat,
Learn from this solemn and serious tale,
How you too can be changed if you'll travel by rail.

SHIRLEY TOULSON

Neighbours

The people who live on the right side of us
Are very quiet and make no fuss,
But the family on the left clatter about
Day and night, and sometimes shout.

Yet the people on the left of us
Are really rather marvellous,
Instead of being put out by everything
They burst out laughing and sing.

But the family who live on the right of us
Often make me curious,
The way the father whispers to the mother,
The sister to her silent brother.

I suppose that neighbours are meant
To be different.

LEONARD CLARK

Poetry Close-up

1. What did Timothy do when 'Daddy fell into the pond'?
2. In the poem 'The Useful Art of Knitting', Mum can do two things at the same time. What are they?
3. Why do you think 'Mum' in Sally Flood's poem has hair which "shows streaks of grey"?
4. In the poem 'The Quarrel', who was it who started making friends? Was it the writer or his brother?
5. Michael Rosen has written a poem about sharing bedrooms. At first he says: "I don't like it" but later he says: "Actually, sharing's all right". Why do you think he changes his mind?
6. Read 'Grandfather' by Susan Hrynkow.
   a) Write down any phrases which you think tell us about Grandfather's job.
   b) What evidence is there that Grandfather was young at heart?
7. Shirley Toulson has written a poem about 'Aunt Kate'.
   a) What made Aunt Kate stop nagging?
   b) Write a humourous story of your own in which someone who nags is made to change their ways.

Other Things To Do

1. Can you describe the personality of one member of your family?
2. Tape record a conversation with one of your grandparents about life when *they* were children.
3. Read one of the 'Supergran' books by Forest Wilson.
4. Can you find out anything about the meaning and origin of your surname?

Children

"Boys are nasty, dirty and mean.
Girls are beautiful, slim and clean."

Do you agree with this view of children?

Below you will find a number of imaginary children who all live in the same street.

Forgetful Fred	Lucky Louise	Greedy Graham	Moaning Martin
Clumsy Clive	Tearful Tina	Lazy Laura	Naughty Neil
Terrible Terence	Horrible Howard	Cheerful Charlie	Perfect Pam
Selfish Sandra	Nattering Nora	Angry Ann	Cowardly Carol

Choose one of these children's names or make one up yourself.

Write a poem or a story about this child. If you read the poems in this section and look at the word list below, you may get some ideas.

wise	scatterbrain	responsible	bully	sociable	secret
din	troublesome	jealous	sob	kind	pest
day-dream	talkative	lively	honest	tolerant	share
clever	generous	helpful	argument	trust	embarrassing

Hands of Friendship

In Britain, many children or their parents were born in other countries. They may have their own culture, and their religion, history, traditions, food, language, clothing, music, art and pastimes could be different.

Use the list below as chapter headings to make your own topic book about a child from one of these countries.

India Greece Hong Kong Italy
West Indies Poland Pakistan

Or — choose a country of your own to study. It would help if you could talk to someone who lives, or used to live, there.

If you turn to page 50 you will find some questions on the poems themselves and some more things to do.

Boys will be boys

Boys will be boys, it's a fact of human nature,
And girls will grow up to be mothers.

Look at little Peter, isn't he a terror?
Shooting all the neighbours with his cowboy gun.
Screaming like a jet plane, always throwing something,
I just can't control him, trouble he's the one.

Ah but boys will be boys, it's a fact of human nature,
And girls will grow up to be mothers.

Look at little Janie. Doesn't she look pretty?
Playing with her dolly, proper little mum.
Never getting dirty, never being naughty —
Don't punch your sister, Peter. Now look what you've done.

Ah but boys will be boys, it's a fact of human nature,
And girls will grow up to be mothers.

What's come over Janie? Janie's turning nasty,
Left hook to the body, right hook in the eye.
Vicious little hussy! Now Peter's started bawling.
What a cissy! Who said you could cry?

Because boys must be boys, it's a fact of human nature,
And girls must grow up to be mothers.

Now things are topsy turvy, Janie wants a football,
Peter just seems happy pushing prams along.
Makes you feel so guilty. Kids are such a worry.
Doctor, doctor, tell me. Where did we go wrong?

Because boys must be boys, it's a fact of human nature,
And girls must grow up to be mothers.

LEON ROSSELSON

Boys

Boys are nasty, dirty and mean.
Girls are beautiful, slim and clean.
Boys slam desk-tops and class-room doors.
They never think of school rules and laws.
When going home,
They thump each other.
When at home,
They try their mother.
They never seem to clean their nails;
Boys should wear curly tails
And have a snubby, grunting nose,
Flappy ears and 'trotter' toes.

S. ROBINSON

from Timothy Winters

Timothy Winters comes to school
With eyes as wide as a football pool,
Ears like bombs and teeth like splinters;
A blitz of a boy is Timothy Winters.

His belly is white, his neck is dark,
And his hair is an exclamation mark.
His clothes are enough to scare a crow
And through his britches the blue winds blow.

CHARLES CAUSLEY

The Boy

Is it, I wonder, a rum thing,
Or nothing to wonder upon,
That whenever a man's doing something
There's always a boy looking on?

If he's mending a road or a motor,
If he's loading a crane or a van,
If he's tinkering at an old boat or
A boot, there's a boy near the man.

If he's climbing a tree or a steeple,
Or shoeing a horse, to the joy
Of a number of on-looking people,
You'll find at his elbow a boy.

If he's wrecking a house, if he's rubbing
A window or building a wall,
Unmoving, unmoved, and past snubbing,
There's a boy in the forefront of all.

If he's doing odd things with the drain-pipes,
If he's pouring hot tar on the street,
Or playing about with the main pipes,
There's a boy almost under his feet.

He may stand for hours like a dumb thing,
But this can be counted upon —
Wherever a man's doing something
There's always a boy looking on.

ELEANOR FARJEON

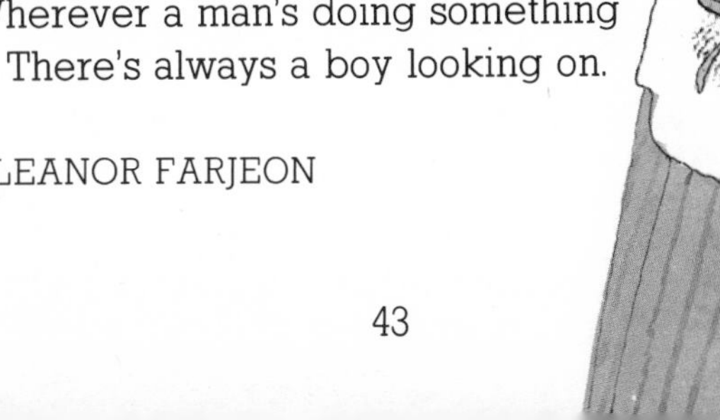

The Story of Fidgety Philip

One evening Philip's father said,
'You twist and squirm and shake your head.
Come, let us see if you are able
To sit quite still for once at table.'
But not a word
Had Philip heard.
He giggled
And wiggled
And wriggled
And tottered
And teetered
And rocked in his chair.
Till his father cried, 'Philip!
Sit still — or beware!'

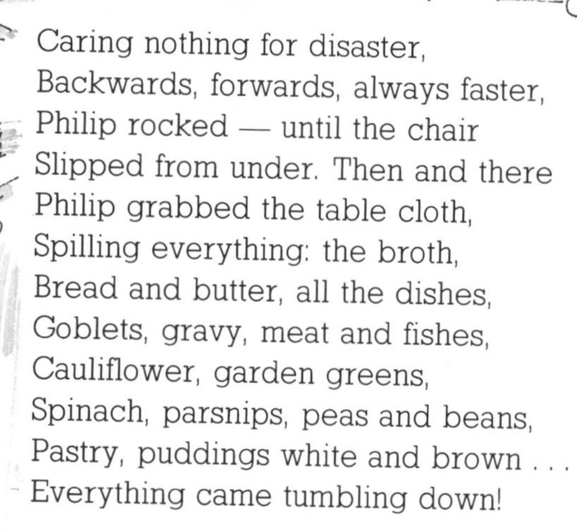

Caring nothing for disaster,
Backwards, forwards, always faster,
Philip rocked — until the chair
Slipped from under. Then and there
Philip grabbed the table cloth,
Spilling everything: the broth,
Bread and butter, all the dishes,
Goblets, gravy, meat and fishes,
Cauliflower, garden greens,
Spinach, parsnips, peas and beans,
Pastry, puddings white and brown . . .
Everything came tumbling down!

Meanwhile where was Philip? There,
Underneath the ruined chair,
Underneath — as you might guess —
Broken plates, a horrid mess,
Groaning in a hideous mood,
Soaked from head to toe with food.
And, to make his plight complete,
Nothing left for him to eat!

HEINRICH HOFFMAN

Sharon's Life

My name is Sharon
I have two brothers
Called Phillip and William
Sometimes they bother me
But often they don't.
Being me is fun.
When it is older
It won't be so good I think.
Phillip lost my book
It had pictures
He lost it
But I am not very cross.
Daddy bought it.
Aunt Judy died last week
Mummy said it was a loss
And then she cried
Quite a bit.
My dog is called Spot
He has some bad habits.
Perhaps I will find the book.
My bed is green.
I'm five.
That's all.
I'm glad I'm alive.

GARETH OWEN

Jemima Jane

Jemima Jane,
  Oh, Jemima Jane,
She loved to go out
  And slosh in the rain.
She loved to go out
  And get herself wet,
And she had a duck
  For her favourite pet.

Every day
  At half-past four
They'd both run out
  The kitchen door;
They'd find a puddle,
  And there they'd stay
Until it was time
  To go away.

They got quite wet,
  But they didn't mind;
And every rainy
  Day they'd find
A new way to splash
  Or a new way to swim.
And the duck loved Jane,
  And Jane loved him.

MARCHETTE CHUTE

Ella McStumping

Ella McStumping
was fond of jumping.
From tables and chairs,
bookshelves and stairs
she would jump to the floor
then climb back for more.
At the age of three
she climbed a high tree
and with one mighty cry
she leapt for the sky.
Doctor McSpetter
says she'll get better,
and the hospital say
she can come home next May,
and Ella McStumping
has given up jumping.

MICHAEL DUGAN

Friends

I fear it's very wrong of me,
And yet I must admit,
When someone offers friendship
I want the *whole* of it.
I don't want everybody else
To share my friends with me.
At least, I want *one* special one,
Who, indisputably,

Likes me much more than all the rest,
Who's always on my side,
Who never cares what others say,
Who lets me come and hide
Within his shadow, in his house
It doesn't matter where —
Who lets me simply be myself,
Who's always, *always* there.

ELIZABETH JENNINGS

What Would You Like to be When You Grow Up, Little Girl?

I'd like to be a model girl, lithe and long and lean;
I'd like to be a TV star, shining from the screen:

I'd like to be an actress, and strut upon the stage;
I'd like to be a poet, printed on this page:

I'd like to be a busy nurse, smoothing down the sheets;
I'd like to be an usherette, and show you to your seats:

I'd like to be a banker, and make a lot of money;
I'd like to be a bee-keeper, and bask on bread and honey:

I'd like to be a dancer, and dance the disco beat;
I'd like to be a traffic warden, storming down the street:

I'd like to be a hairdresser, with blower, brush and comb;
I'd like to be a Romany, the whole wide world to roam:

I'd like to be an air hostess, and soar across the seas;
I'd like to be a doctor, and dose you when you sneeze:

I'd like to be in Parliament, and speak a speech to you;
I'd like to be a High Court Judge, and try a case or two:

I'd like to be a teacher, and quell you with one look;
I'd like to be an artist, and illustrate this book:

I'd like to be a gymnast, and balance on a bar;
I'd like to be a grand chauffeur, and drive a dashing car:

I'd like to be a skater, racing round a rink;
I'd like to be just *anything* . . . I think!

JENNY CRAIG

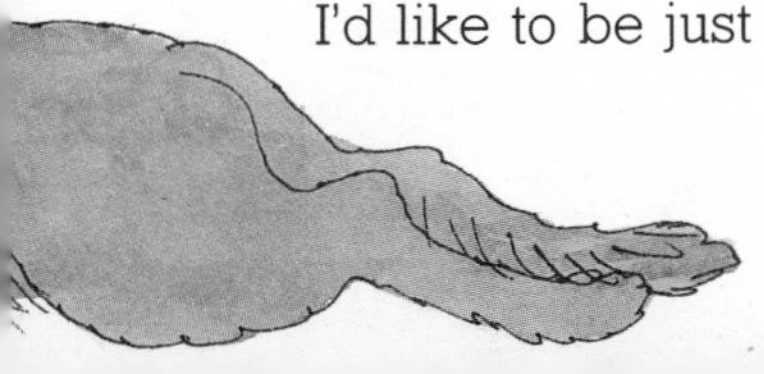

When you're a GROWN-UP

When you're a GROWN-UP
a SERIOUS and SENSIBLE PERSON
When you've stopped being SILLY
you can go out and have babies
and go into a SERIOUS and SENSIBLE shop
and ask for:
Tuftytails, Paddipads, Bikkipegs, Cosytoes
and
Tommy Tippee Teethers.
Sno-bunnies, Visivents, Safeshines
Comfybaths, Dikkybibs
and
Babywipes.
Rumba Rattles and Trigger Jiggers
A Whirlee Three, a Finger Flip
or A Quacky Duck.
And if you're very SENSIBLE
you can choose
Easifitz, Babybuggies and a Safesitterstand.
Or is it a
Saferstandsit?
No it's a Sitstandsafe. I can never remember.
I'm sorry but Babytalk is a very difficult language.
It's for adults only.
Like 'X' films
Much too horrible for children.

MICHAEL ROSEN

Growing Up

I know a lad called Billy
Who goes along with me
He plays this game
Where he uses my name
And makes people think that he's me.

Don't ever mess with Billy
He's a vicious sort of bloke
He'll give you a clout
For saying nowt
And thump you for a joke.

My family can't stand Billy
Can't bear him round the place
He won't eat his food
He's always rude
And wears scowls all over his face.

No one can ever break Billy
He's got this look in his eye
That seems to say
You can whale me all day
But you'll not make Billy cry.

He has a crazy face has Billy
Eyes that look but can't see
A mouth like a latch
Ears that don't match
And a space where his brains should be.

Mad Billy left one morning
Crept away without being seen
Left his body for me
That fits perfectly
And a calm where his madness had been.

GARETH OWEN

Poetry Close-up

1. Read the poem 'The Story of Fidgety Philip' by Heinrich Hoffman.
   a) What did his father want Philip to do?
   b) How do you know that Philip didn't take any notice?
   c) What word does the poet use that means 'soup'?
   d) Why did all the food fall from the table?
2. a) In Eleanor Farjeon's poem 'The Boy', how many different jobs are mentioned?
   b) Which, of all these jobs, would you like to stand and watch? Why?
3. a) Which animal does S. Robinson think boys resemble?
   b) Can you compare the girls in the poem to any type of animal?
   c) Explain why you agree or disagree with the poem.

Other Things To Do

1. What do the initials NSPCC stand for? Find out the address of this organisation and compose a class letter to it, asking for details of the society's work.
2. Can you think of a boy's and a girl's Christian name for each letter of the alphabet? Make a list.
3. Draw a 'silhouette' of one of your friends.
4. Choose one of the characters from page 40 and make up a 'comic strip' of one of their adventures.

Going to School

"The school where I work and play each day
Is made of stone and old and grey".

Does this school sound like yours?

Here is a collection of thoughts and ideas about school. Read them and then read the poems which follow.

.... Think of — lining up .... sitting still .... morning assembly .... all kinds of teachers .... wet playtimes .... school bully .... making new friends .... squabbles and arguments .... being in trouble .... kind dinner ladies .... class visits .... going swimming .... school teams .... sports day .... seeing the headteacher .... favourite lessons .... tidying up .... crowded class-rooms .... busy caretakers .... after-school clubs .... school concerts .... parents' evening .... breaking up.

What does school mean to you? Try to write a poem about your own feelings on school. These words may help you:

silence	display	topic	chase	numbers
concentrate	boring	stimulating	whistle	noisy
stern	interesting	embarrass	talkative	exciting
tears	enthusiasm	shout	routine	fights
rewards	frightened	punishment	lazy	

School Days

Find out all you can about the history of your own school.

What were schools like in Victorian times? Draw and write all you can about the lessons, class-rooms, teachers, and anything else you discover.

Now write about 'My school in the year 2100'.

If you turn to page 60 you will find some questions on the poems themselves and some more things to do.

The School

The houses are red and tall or small
With brown birds perched on the backyard wall.
The school where I work and play each day
Is made of stone and old and grey,
And rain can't wash away the soot
That covers it from head to foot.
It's full as a parcel of girls and boys,
Drawings, paintings, writing, toys,
Dinners, teachers, pets and noise.

STANLEY COOK

Impressions of a New Boy

This school is huge — I hate it!
Please take me home.
Steep stairs cut in stone,
Peeling ceiling far too high,
The Head said 'Wait' so I wait alone,
Alone though Mum stands here, close by.

The voice is loud — I hate it!
Please take me home.

'Come. Sit. What is your name?'
Trembling lips. The words won't come.
The Head says 'Speak,' but my cheeks flame,
I hear him give a quiet sigh.

The room is full — I hate it.
Please take me home.

A sea of faces stare at me,
My desk is much too small,
Its wooden ridge rubs my knee,
But Head said 'Sit' so though I'm tall
I know that I must try.

The yard is full — I hate it,
Please take me home.

Bodies jostle me away,
Pressing me against the wall.
Then one boy says, 'Want to play?'
The boy says, 'Catch' and throws a ball,
And playtime seems to fly.

This school is great — I love it.

MARIAN COLLIHOLE

First Day at School

A millionbillionwillion miles from home
Waiting for the bell to go. (To go where?)
Why are they all so big, other children?
So noisy? So much at home they
must have been born in uniform
Lived all their lives in playgrounds
Spent the years inventing games
that don't let me in. Games
that are rough, that swallow you up.

And the railings.
All around, the railings.
Are they to keep out wolves and monsters?
Things that carry off and eat children?
Things you don't take sweets from?
Perhaps they're to stop us getting out
Running away from the lessins. Lessin.
What does a lessin look like?
Sounds small and slimy.
They keep them in glassrooms.
Whole rooms made out of glass. Imagine.

I wish I could remember my name
Mummy said it would come in useful.
Like wellies. When there's puddles.
Yellowwellies. I wish she was here.
I think my name is sewn on somewhere
Perhaps the teacher will read it for me.
Tea-cher. The one who makes the tea.

ROGER McGOUGH

Bus to School

Rounding a corner
It comes to a stay.
Quick! Grab the rail!
Now we're off on our way . . .
Oh, but it's Thursday,
The day of fear! —
Three hateful lessons!
And school draws near.

Here in the bus though
There's plenty to see:
Boys full of talk about
Last night's TV;
Girls with their violins,
Armfuls of twigs
And flowers for teacher;
Bartlett and Biggs;
Conductor who chats with them,
Jokes about cricket;
Machine that flicks out
A white ribbon of ticket . . .
Yes, but it's Thursday,
The day of fear! —
Six hateful lessons!
And school draws near.

Conductor now waiting,
Firm as a rock,
For Billy, whose penny's
Slid down in his sock.
Conductor frowning,
With finger on handle;
Poor Billy blushes,
Undoes his sandal . . .
"Hold very tight, please!
Any more fares?"
Whistling conductor
Goes clumping upstairs . . .
Boots up above, now!
Boys coming down! . . .
Over the hump-bridge
And into the town.

Old Warren sweeping
In his shirt-sleeves
Sun on his shop-front,
Sun on the leaves . . .
Only, it's Thursday,
The day of fear! —
All hateful lessons!
And school draws near.

JOHN WALSH

The Lollipop Lady

The Lollipop Lady is not
as tall as the lollipop
but she shines in the wet.
Some days I forget
about her, and stop
with a skid in a puddle
and there is her red and white bubble
all of a sudden, twice.
The Lollipop Lady is nice;
she sorts out the muddle
and holds my hand
and stops the cars with her magic wand
so I can walk, where there aren't any stripes,
past huge big lorries and motor bikes
which roar and shake and
smoke like dragons; but all of them wait
for the Lollipop Lady's wave —
for the children. When she
smiles and nods at me
I can cross the road. If I'm as brave
as her when I grow up, *I* could be
a shining Lollipop Lady.

JANE WHITTLE

He who owns the whistle rules the world

january wind and the sun
playing truant again.
Rain beginning to scratch
its fingernails across
the blackboard sky

in the playground
kids dive-bomb, corner
at silverstone or execute
traitors. Armed
with my Acme Thunderer
I step outside,
take a deep breath
and bring the world
to a standstill

ROGER McGOUGH

My Picture

My flame-picture painting
is pinned on the wall
and teacher says
it's a rainbow ball.

But though I'm pleased
I sometimes frown —
Dare I tell her today
it's upside down?

ARCHIE BARRETT

In the Playground

In the playground
Some run round
Chasing a ball
Or chasing each other;
Some pretend to be
Someone on TV;
Some walk
And talk,
Some stand
On their hands
Against the wall
And some do nothing at all.

STANLEY COOK

Rodge Said

Rodge said,
'Teachers — they want it all ways —
You're jumping up and down on a chair
or something
and they grab hold of you and say
"Would you do that sort of thing in your own home?"

'So you say, "No."
And they say,
"Well don't do it here then,"

'But if you say, "Yes, I do it at home."
they say,
"Well, we don't want that sort of thing
going on here
thank you very much."

'Teachers — they get you all ways,'
Rodge said.

MICHAEL ROSEN

Out of School

Four o'clock strikes,
There's a rising hum,
Then the doors fly open,
The children come.

With a wild catcall
And a hopscotch hop
And a bouncing ball
And a whirling top.

Grazing of knees,
A hair-pull and a slap,
A hitched-up satchel,
A pulled-down cap,

Bully boys reeling off,
Hurt ones squealing off,
Aviators wheeling off,
Mousy ones stealing off,

Woollen gloves for chilblains,
Cotton rags for snufflers,
Pigtails, coat-tails,
Tails of mufflers,

Machine-gun cries,
A kennelful of snarlings,
A hurricane of leaves,
A treeful of starlings,

Thinning away now
By some and some,
Thinning away, away,
All gone home.

HAL SUMMERS

Mr Fitzsimmons

Mr. Fitzsimmons,
Our caretaker, is tall
For reaching pictures
Down from the wall,
Looking over gates
And piled-up crates.
Just the height
To put new bulbs
In electric lights
Or discover
What was lost
On top of cupboards.
He has a key
Worn shiny in his pocket
For every door
And a polisher
Plugging in at the socket
For every floor.
He brushes school clean
And polishes it bright
Every night.

STANLEY COOK

Parents' Evening

Tonight your mum and dad go off to school.
The class-room's empty.
Rabbit and gerbil sleep.
Your painting's with the others on the wall,
And all the projects you have ever done,
The long-since-finished and the just-begun,
Are ranged on desks.
Your books are in a pile.
'He gets his fractions right,' your teacher says.
Your mother reads your 'news',
Is pleased to find you've prominently listed
The sticky pudding that you liked last Tuesday.

Suppose one evening you could go along
To see how mum and dad had spent their days,
What sort of work would you find up on show?
Bus-loads of people,
Towers of coins,
Letters to fill a hundred postmen's sacks,
Hayricks of dust from offices and houses,
Plates, cakes, trains, clothes,
Stretches of motorways and bridges,
Aeroplanes and bits of ships,
Bulldozers and paper-clips,
'Cellos and pneumatic drills.
A noise to make the sleepy gerbil stir.

SHIRLEY TOULSON

Poetry Close-up

1. In Stanley Cook's poem, what jobs can Mr. Fitzsimmons do because he is tall?
2. As you read through the poem 'Bus to School' by John Walsh, the number of hateful lessons increases. Why do you think this happens?
3. What reasons are given for hating school in 'Impressions of a New Boy' by Marian Collihole? Why does the new boy change his mind?
4. In 'First Day at School' by Roger McGough, what ideas does the new child have that are wrong?
5. Why does Jane Whittle think the lollipop lady is brave in her poem?
6. Read the second verse of Shirley Toulson's 'Parents' Evening'. What jobs would be represented by the work on show?

Other Things To Do

1. Find any information you can about schools in other countries. Choose one country and make a booklet about schools there.
2. What is the 'catchment area' of your school? Find a large scale map of your area and pin-point where the children in your class live.
3. Draw and colour a picture showing everything described in Stanley Cook's poem 'The School'.

People at Work

> "There's not a place I'd rather be
> Than working round machinery".

These lines describe one particular type of work. Read the poems in this section to find out about other jobs. Then think about these questions.

How have jobs changed over the years?

.... Think of — coachman and jet pilot .... town crier and newscaster .... wheelwright and production-line worker .... ledger clerk and computer operator.

Where would you like to work?

.... Think of — a busy office .... a quiet library
.... a large factory .... the open countryside
.... a childrens' nursery .... your own shop.

If you wish to write your own poem, these words might help you.

career	occupation	skilled	din	hustle	equipment
uniform	conveyor	commute	chatter	project	market
advert	overalls	shift	routine	bored	diligent
bustle	trade	efficient	machinery	interesting	challenging

Children as Workers

In the last century, young children worked in factories and down mines. Find out what types of jobs they did, how much they were paid, and what hours they worked.

Lord Shaftesbury was very influential in getting child labour abolished. Find out all you can about him.

If you turn to page 74 you will find some questions on the poems themselves and some more things to do.

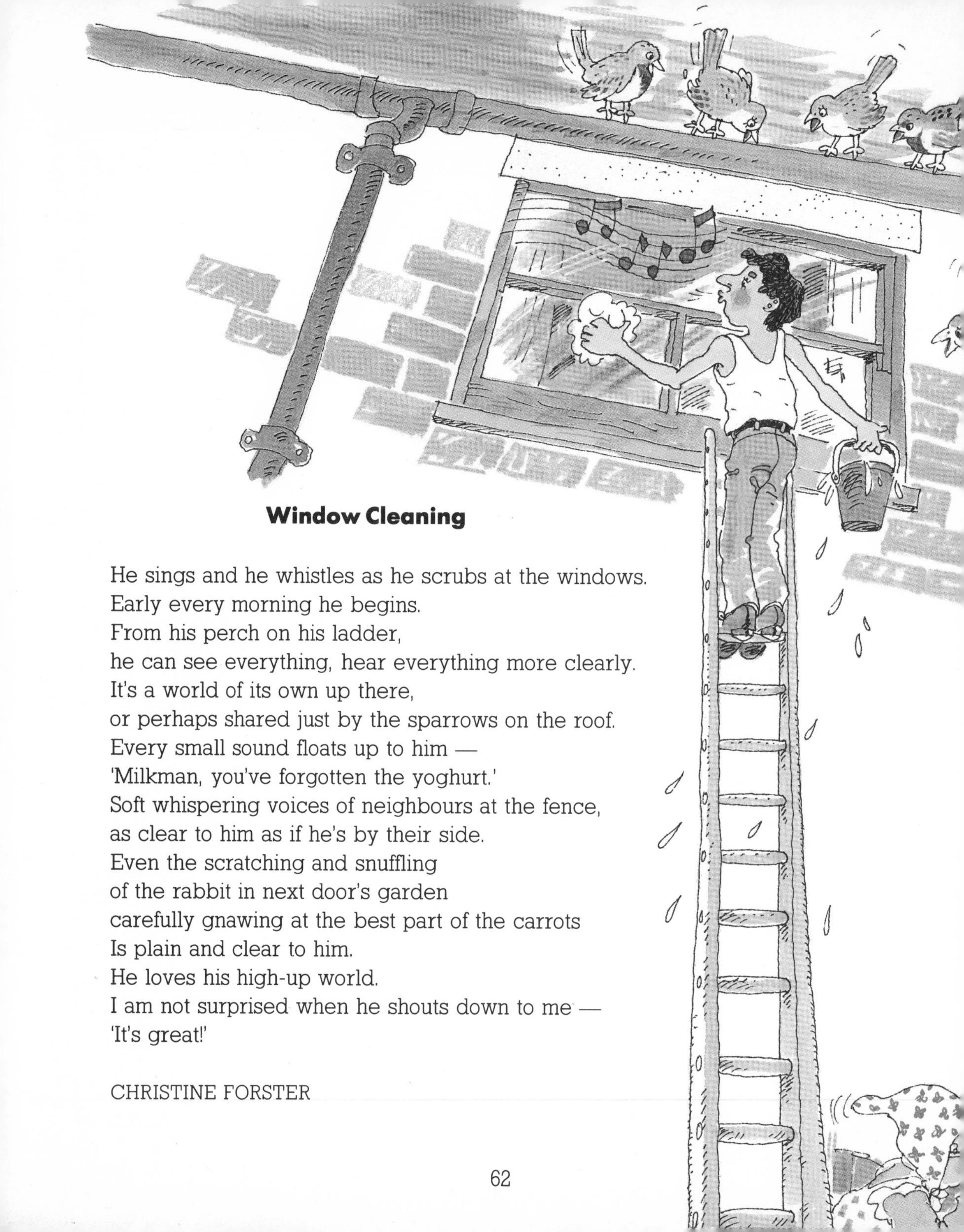

Window Cleaning

He sings and he whistles as he scrubs at the windows.
Early every morning he begins.
From his perch on his ladder,
he can see everything, hear everything more clearly.
It's a world of its own up there,
or perhaps shared just by the sparrows on the roof.
Every small sound floats up to him —
'Milkman, you've forgotten the yoghurt.'
Soft whispering voices of neighbours at the fence,
as clear to him as if he's by their side.
Even the scratching and snuffling
of the rabbit in next door's garden
carefully gnawing at the best part of the carrots
Is plain and clear to him.
He loves his high-up world.
I am not surprised when he shouts down to me —
'It's great!'

CHRISTINE FORSTER

from **The Dustbin Men**

The older ones have gone to school,
My breakfast's on the plate,
But I can't leave the window-pane,
I might be just too late.

I've heard the clatter down the street,
I know they're creeping near,
The team of gruff-voiced, burly men
Who keep our dustbins clear.

And I must watch and see them clang
The dustbins on the road,
And stand in pairs to heave up high
The double-handled load.

Yes, there they come, the lorry growls
And grinds in bottom gear;
The dustman knees the garden gate
As, high up by his ear,
Firmly he balances the bin,
Head tilted to one side;
The great mouth of the rubbish cart
Is yawning very wide;
To me the mouth looks like a beast's,
A dragon's hungry jaws
That snap the refuse out of sight
Behind those sliding doors.

GREGORY HARRISON

Postman's Knock

Rattat! Rattat!
  There's the postman at the door,
He always knocks like that,
  No matter who it's for.
It may be a letter
  And it might be a box,
So I'm always very glad
  When the postman knocks.

Rattat! Rattat!
  Shall I run along to see
If he is on the mat
  With something meant for me?
It may be just a postcard,
  But it might be a box,
So I always run to look
When the postman knocks.

RODNEY BENNETT

Sooeep

Black as a chimney is his face,
And ivory white his teeth,
And in his brass-bound cart he rides,
The chestnut blooms beneath.

'Sooeep, Sooeep!' he cries, and brightly peers
This way and that, to see
With his two light-blue shining eyes
What custom there may be.

And once inside the house, he'll squat,
And drive his rods on high.
Till twirls his sudden sooty brush
Against the morning sky.

Then, 'mid his bulging bags of soot,
With half the world asleep,
His small cart wheels him off again,
Still hoarsely bawling, 'Sooeep!'

WALTER DE LA MARE

The Barber

I'd like to be a barber, and learn to shave and clip,
Calling out, 'Next, please!' and pocketing my tip.
All day you'd hear my scissors going, 'Snip, Snip, Snip!'
I'd lather people's faces, and their noses I would grip
While I shaved most carefully along the upper lip.
But I wouldn't be a barber if
The razor was to slip.
Would you?

C.J. DENNIS

The Porter

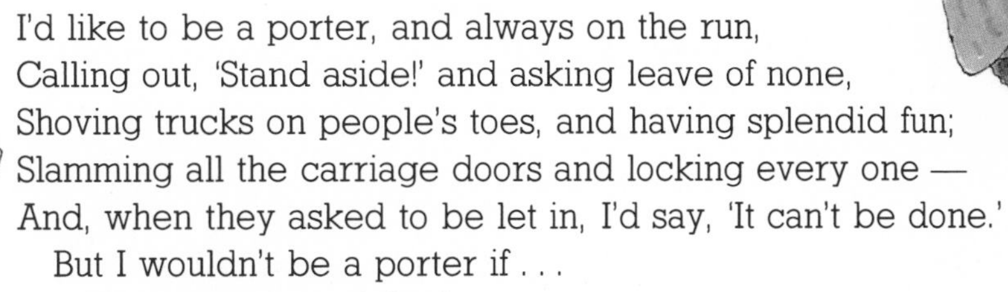

I'd like to be a porter, and always on the run,
Calling out, 'Stand aside!' and asking leave of none,
Shoving trucks on people's toes, and having splendid fun;
Slamming all the carriage doors and locking every one —
And, when they asked to be let in, I'd say, 'It can't be done.'
But I wouldn't be a porter if . . .
The luggage weighed a ton.
Would you?

C.J. DENNIS

The Cobbler

Shoes on counter, bench and shelf;
  Shoes heaped on the floor —
And a golden giant's boot that swings
  Above the Cobbler's door.

Stubby toes and run-down heels;
  Leather soles worn thin;
Shoes so cracked and shiny that
  They positively grin.

Muddy shoes like tired tramps;
  Dancing slippers new —
Cobbler, as you mend them all,
  Do they talk to you?

Do they tell you what they've seen
  On the roads they know?
Do they say what sort of folk
  Take them to and fro?

Are they glad to rest themselves
  In your shop awhile,
Or are they eager to be off
  Mile after mile?

Does the golden boot outside,
  Hanging by itself,
Wish it were a plain, patched shoe,
  Cobbler, on your shelf?

RACHEL FIELD

The Florist

Florist shops are beautiful,
All damply green and dimly cool,
And the men who keep them are sure to be
A little baggy about the knee,
With voices pleasant and rather low
From living alone with things that grow;
For you can't stay noisy and hurried where
Petal on petal fills the air
With spiciness, and every tree
Is hung with gayest greenery.
Grocers bustle and butchers shout,
Tradesmen tramp noisily in and out,
But florists are quiet men and kind,
With a sort of fragrance of the mind.

RACHEL FIELD

The Dressmaker

Mrs Binns
Mrs Binns
Fills her mouth with
Safety-pins;

Now and then she
Takes one out,
Turns and twiddles
Me about.

Talking, as she
Pricks my hip,
Through the corner
Of her lip.

While she lengthens,
Cuts, and measures,
Still her tongue
Confines her treasures . . .

How I long
To move and see
If she'd swallow
Two or three!

But Mrs Binns
Is very clever
For she never
Never never
Swallows any
Of her pins.
I wish I were
Mrs Binns!

JEAN KENWARD

The Fire Station

As I went by
The tall thin tower
Where the hoses
Hang to dry
And the big glass doors
With fire-engines
Redder than fire
Lined up inside,
A bell began to ring
Fluttering
Its metal tongue
On its metal lips
And men from upstairs
Slid down a pole
And hurried on
Coats and helmets.
The fire-engines started,
The doors were opened wide
And a man went into the road
To stop the cars.

Sirens shouted out
A warning sound
And flashing blue lights
Were spinning round.
People came out of shops
To stand and stare
And buses pulled
Into the side.
The bright red engines,
The hurrying men,
The revolving lights
The shouting sirens
And busy bell
Were more exciting
Than the fire itself.

STANLEY COOK

Sandwich Men

There's something about Sandwich Men
  That makes me want to cry; —
Not just because they're mostly old
  And dreary round the eye,
Or stooped between those painted boards
  Their shoulders carry high,
It's something that you seem to feel
  When Sandwich Men go by.

You always know that they are there
  No matter how you try
To turn your head the other way;
  It's not because they sigh
Or beg. They haven't things to sell
  And so you cannot buy.
You have to watch them shuffle past
  In rainy streets or dry,
And feel that something that you feel
  When Sandwich Men go by.

RACHEL FIELD

Dan the Watchman

Dan the Watchman
Doesn't go to bed.
He sits in a little wooden hut
Instead;
At a little coke fire,
Half red, half blue,
Listening to the owls
Go 'Whoo! Whoo! Whoo!'
And the Town Hall clock
Strike half-past two.

When the moon sits on top
Of the grey church spire,
He puts more coke
On his red-and-blue fire,
When the old mill pond
Begins to freeze,
He eats his supper
Of bread and cheese.

I'd like to go out
In the middle of the night
When the little coke fire
Is shining bright,
When the flames turn blue
And the flames burn red,
And everyone else in the world is in bed.
Then I'd sit in the little wooden hut with Dan
And drink strong tea from his black billycan.

JOHN D. SHERIDAN

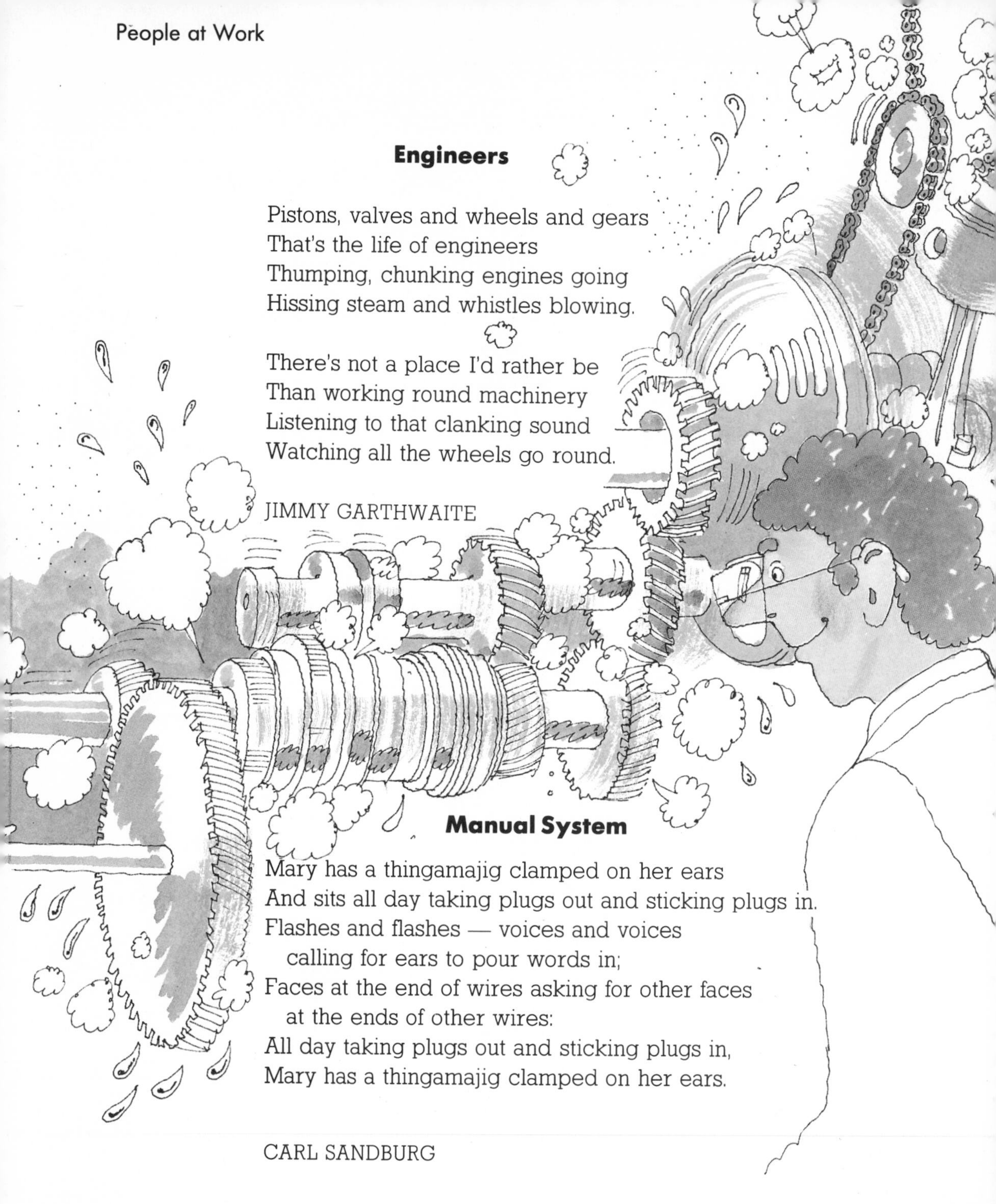

Engineers

Pistons, valves and wheels and gears
That's the life of engineers
Thumping, chunking engines going
Hissing steam and whistles blowing.

There's not a place I'd rather be
Than working round machinery
Listening to that clanking sound
Watching all the wheels go round.

JIMMY GARTHWAITE

Manual System

Mary has a thingamajig clamped on her ears
And sits all day taking plugs out and sticking plugs in.
Flashes and flashes — voices and voices
calling for ears to pour words in;
Faces at the end of wires asking for other faces
at the ends of other wires:
All day taking plugs out and sticking plugs in,
Mary has a thingamajig clamped on her ears.

CARL SANDBURG

Nurse

Now I'll take your temp'rature,
If you please, sir.
Don't chew that thermometer,
And keep still, please, sir.

See me put the little dots
Up and down the chart,
And wheel the shining instruments
On a big glass cart,
Give the patients medicine
And tuck them up in bed,
Make them laugh when they are sad
And see that they are fed.

I make them do as they are told,
For I'm the nurse, you see,
And when I'm busy in the ward
I'm happy as can be.

M. HOWGATE

The Squirrel

We watched the old man carving; his fingers moved
The delicate tools upon the crimson wood.
In the dark of the crowded little workroom
We followed his fingers and, breathless, leaned and stood,
Till out of the jumble of nails and hammers and saws,
In the little room, he held in his hands a squirrel,
With crimson fur, bright eyes, a nut in its paws.

SYLVIA READ

Poetry Close-up

1. In the poem 'The Dressmaker', what are the 'treasures' Mrs Binns' tongue confines?
2. Read the poem 'The Fire Station'. What were more exciting than the fire itself?
3. a) What is Mary's job in the poem 'Manual System' by Carl Sandburg?
   b) What is the 'thingamajig' clamped on her ears?
4. John Sheridan in his poem 'Dan the Watchman' mentions a 'billycan'. What does he mean?
5. Read the poem 'Sandwich Men'.
   a) What do these men do?
   b) Why do you think they are called sandwich men?
6. Imagine that you are apprenticed to a 'Sooeep'. Write a story about a day working with him.

Other Things To Do

1. In the world of work things are changing very quickly. Some of the jobs mentioned in this section are now out of date or are now done in different ways. Can you find any examples of these changes in the poems? Write a little about how and why they have occurred.
2. Describe in detail all the jobs you think your teacher has to do.
3. Choose one job you do at home and draw a step-by-step guide which would help a non-English-speaking person to do it correctly.
4. Make a topic book about jobs which need a uniform.

Likes and Dislikes

'The Fair' and 'Taking Medicine' are the titles of two poems in this section. Most children would enjoy going to the fair but not taking medicine. Do you agree? Read all the poems in this section and then think about these questions.

What do you like?

.... Think of — playing with friends .... opening presents .... interesting hobbies .... days out .... favourite programmes .... special meals.

What do you dislike?

.... Think of — a doctor's needle .... the dentist's chair .... the sight of blood .... going shopping .... tests and exams .... rainy days .... dark nights.

If you wish to write your own poems, these words may help you.

illness	disgusting	excitement	ache	pleasure
detest	terrifying	valuable	delicious	clammy
wince	abhor	bored	sour	tasty
attractive	bitter	pain	scream	grimace
dreaded	loathe	lovable	sweet	

Out of School

Are you a member of a club or society? If not, do you have your own special hobby outside school? It could be the Cubs or Brownies, fishing or stamp-collecting, dancing or gymnastics.

Make a booklet about your favourite interest. It might include a short history, any important rules, famous personalities who are involved, clothing worn and equipment used, plus any other details you wish to mention. Use cuttings, photographs and drawings to illustrate your work.

If you turn to page 84 you will find some questions on the poems themselves and some more things to do.

The Fair

Riding horses, swinging high,
Helter skelter, round we fly.
Flashing lights and noise and bustle,
Laughing crowds all in a hustle.

Slowly the big wheel turns around,
Up and up, far from the ground.
Stopping here and stopping there,
Hanging high up in the air.

Tiny people down below
Wave as higher still we go;
We see far, far beyond the town,
Then come slowly, slowly down.

Guns go bang, and hoop-las fly.
Roll up, roll up, come and try!
Toffee apples here to eat,
Candy floss all pink and sweet.

Balloons and dolls for us to buy,
Coconuts for us to shy.
Fun and games for all to share —
We all enjoy the jolly fair.

E.M. STANTON

Speedway Racing

They line up together,
These monsters of speed,
Then, quicker than lightning,
There's some in the lead.
They come to a corner
Most dreaded of all,
Too closely they take it
And three of them fall.
But on go the rest
With a rush and a roar,
Faster and faster
Than ever before;
The favourite foremost,
His rival behind,
They take the last turning,
Up-curving and blind.
The leader leaps forward,
And then the flag drops,
He cuts off his engine,
And soon as he stops,
And lifts up his helmet,
Then loud in his ears
Rings thunder of clapping,
And cheers upon cheers.

ANA BALDUQUE

Denis Law

I live at 14 Stanhope Street,
Me Mum, me Dad and me,
And three of us have made a gang,
John Stokes and Trev and me.

Our favourite day is Saturday;
We go Old Trafford way
And wear red colours in our coats
To watch United play.

We always stand behind the goal
In the middle of the roar.
The others come to see the game —
I come for Denis Law.

His red sleeves flap around his wrists,
He's built all thin and raw,
But the toughest backs don't stand a chance
When the ball's near Denis Law.

He's a whiplash when he's in control,
He can swivel like an eel,
And twist and sprint in such a way
It makes defences reel.

And when he's hurtling for the goal
I know he's got to score.
Defences may stop normal men —
They can't stop Denis Law.

We all race home when full time blows
To kick a tennis ball,
And Trafford Park is our back-yard,
And the stand is next door's wall.

Old Stokesey shouts, 'I'm Jimmy Greaves,'
And scores against the door,
And Trev shouts: 'I'll be Charlton,' —
But I am Denis Law.

GARETH OWEN

Action Man

Polar explorer
Action Man
Covers his ears with fur
In his bright red hood
And puts his ski-ing boots on.
As he bends his knees
And crouches over his skis
It begins to freeze.
Snowy mountains rise
Into frosty skies
And over the snow
He swoops towards the Pole.

Action Man puts on jump-boots
And parachute.
As he fastens his helmet
Under his chin
Clouds gather round
Looking like the ceiling
Of the roof of the world
Where they live
To people below
And, pulling the ripcord,
Through the ceiling
The Red Devil dives.

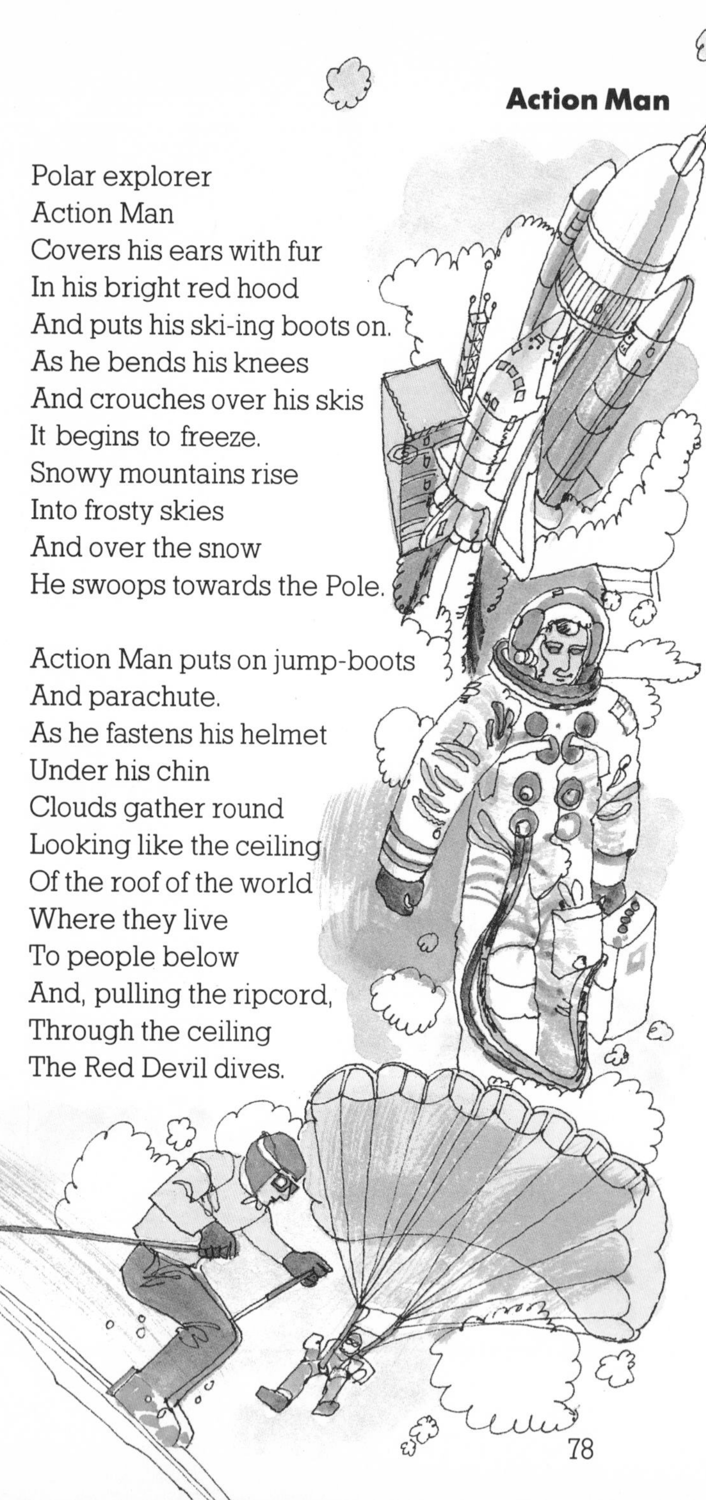

Action Man puts on his silver suit
And heavily weighted boots.
As he puts his head
Inside his helmet
The countdown has started;
There is his rocket
Pointed like a pencil,
Ready to dot
A landing spot
On the moon.
Beneath it the fuel flares
And like an extra star
It shoots through the air.

The winds give a lion-like roar
And huge waves somersault
Like elephants on to the shore
As eagle-eyed Action Man
Puts his equipment on
And with his crew
Speeds to the rescue
In a motor boat
Or lowers a rope
From a twirling, whirling
Helicopter
While savage waves beneath
Snap their hungry teeth;
But nothing can
Frighten Action Man.

STANLEY COOK

Toffee-Slab

As thick as a plank, as unbending as Fate,
It was wrapped in wax-paper, and weighed like a slate;
It had a brown cow on it, smiling and fat,
With 'rich' and 'creamy' and grand words like that:

And you broke it with bricks on Mrs Doig's wall,
So it came out irregular, but with something for all
(If you were quick, it was more or less fair —
Even Wee Andy had his proportional share);

Then with nobody speaking, with sort of fixed grins
And oozings like glue leaking over our chins
We'd stand there for ages, our eyes staring wide,
The great splinters of it jammed tightly inside,

With the sharpest end stuck, up near your brain,
What pleasure! — mingled with twinges of pain.

BRIAN LEE

What do you collect?

What do you collect?
Coins, dolls from other lands?
Or jokes that no one understands?

What do you collect?
Skulls, posters, badges, bells?
Or walking-sticks, or seaside shells?

What do you collect?
Stamps, gem stones, model cars?
Or wrappers torn from chocolate bars?

What do you collect?
Leaves, photographs of cats?
Or horror masks and rubber bats?

What do you collect?
Books, fossils, records, rocks?
Or comics in a cardboard box?

WES MAGEE

I'm so mad I could scream!

I'm so mad I could scream,
I'm so mad I could spit,
Turn over a table,
Run off in a snit!

I'm so mad I could yell,
I could tear out my hair,
Throw a rock through a window,
Or wrestle a bear!

I mean — I am furious,
In a terrible huff,
I'm raging and roaring
And boy, am I tough!

I'm really ferocious,
I really am *mad*,
I'm ready to beat up
My mother and dad!

On thinking it over,
I *will not* leave home,
But I'll put all my anger
Right here in this poem.

I'm feeling much better —
Like peaches and cream —
For a poem is the best way
Of letting off steam!

WILLIAM COLE

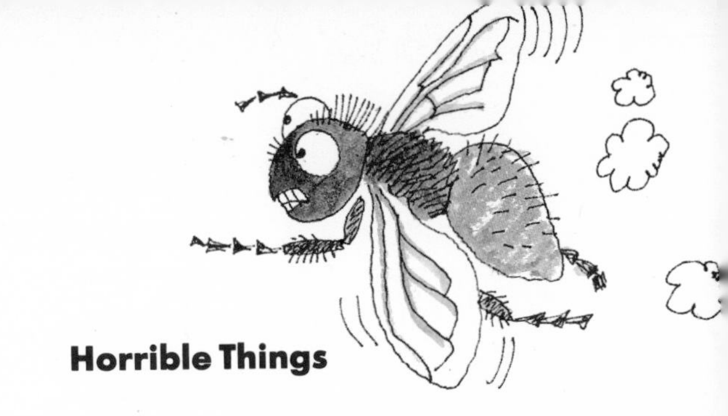

Horrible Things

'What's the horriblest thing you've seen?'
Said Nell to Jean.

'Some grey-coloured, trodden-on plasticine;
On a plate, a left-over cold baked bean;
A cloak-room ticket numbered thirteen;
A slice of meat without any lean;
The smile of a spiteful fairy-tale queen;
A thing in the sea like a brown submarine;
A cheese fur-coated in brilliant green;
A bluebottle perched on a piece of sardine.
What's the horriblest thing *you've* seen?'
Said Jean to Nell.

'Your face, as you tell
Of all the horriblest things you've seen.'

ROY FULLER

Taking Medicine

In the bedroom I hide,
Mother calls,
My sister reads,
And I am silent,
I go to her very gravely going as silently and slowly as I can,
Suddenly I rush into the kitchen,
I say, quick, to get it over and done with,
With hot eyes I see mother pouring it out,
I bite the spoon the last drop,
Here I go,
When I have finished I run up the hall shouting,
'I have had my medicine go and have yours.'

VALERIE SEEKINGS

A Little Girl I Hate

I saw a little girl I hate
And kicked her with my toes.
She turned
And smiled
And KISSED me!
Then she punched me on the nose.

ARNOLD SPILKA

Joan Who Hates Parties

Today's little Doreen's party-day;
And it all begins when I'm snatched from play
By Mother, who cries with a gay little laugh,
'Now come along first and have a nice bath!'
And off come my jeans and I'm dumped straight in,
And splashed all over from toes to chin;
Then dumped out again on the big bath-mat —
And don't I just hate that!

For the next half-hour I am rubbed rough-dry,
And tickled with talc till I'm ready to cry,
And perched half-dressed on a backless chair
For the fight between Mother and me and my hair;
Then on go the shoes and the clean white socks,
and the dreamiest of dream-like nylon frocks,
With a sweet blue bow for the end of my plait —
And don't I just hate that!

But I'm ready at last; and at ten-past four
I'll be dropped at dear little Doreen's door;
And at Doreen's door I'll be met with a hearty
Welcome to dear little Doreen's party;
But they won't see me — they won't see Joan —
But a girl with a heart like a thunder-stone;
A girl with the face of a fierce tom-cat . . .
And won't they just hate that!

JOHN WALSH

Poetry Close-up

1. Read John Walsh's poem. What do you think Joan hates most about going to parties?
2. E.M. Stanton has written a poem about 'The Fair'.
   a) What 'rides' are mentioned?
   b) What can be bought to eat?
3. Why do you think the 'Toffee-Slab' would be painful to eat?
4. In the poem 'Action Man', with what is the rocket compared as it travels on its journey?
5. Ana Balduque has written about 'Speedway Racing'.
   a) How does the winner of the race stop his machine?
   b) What causes three riders to fall?
6. Imagine you are the inventor of the most 'fantastic' fairground ride in the world.
   Describe the ride in the most exciting way you can.
7. 'Denis Law' was Gareth Owen's childhood hero.
   Write a poem or an account of someone you admire.

Other Things To Do

1. Design a poster to advertise a travelling fair.
2. 'Most things we like are bad for us'.
   Discuss this with your friends.
3. Make two bar charts showing:
   a) The school lessons your class enjoys most;
   b) The school lessons your class enjoys least.
4. Write about those parts of the area where you live that you like or dislike.

Funny People

"The folk who live in Backward Town
Are inside out and upside down".

The poems in this section are about people who will make you laugh. You may want to write your own poem about an imaginary, comical person.

Here are some words and phrases to help you.

If you turn to page 96 you will find some more things to do.

Colonel Fazackerley

Colonel Fazackerley Butterworth-Toast
Bought an old castle complete with a ghost,
But someone or other forgot to declare
To Colonel Fazack that the spectre was there.

On the very first evening, while waiting to dine,
The Colonel was taking a fine sherry wine,
When the ghost, with a furious flash and a flare,
Shot out of the chimney and shivered, 'Beware!'

Colonel Fazackerley put down his glass
And said, 'My dear fellow, that's really first class!
I just can't conceive how you do it at all.
I imagine you're going to a Fancy Dress Ball?'

At this the dread ghost gave a withering cry.
Said the Colonel (his monocle firm in his eye),
'Now just how you do it I wish I could think.
Do sit down and tell me, and please have a drink.'

The ghost in his phosphorous cloak gave a roar
And floated about between ceiling and floor.
He walked through a wall and returned through a pane
And backed up the chimney and came down again.

Said the Colonel, 'With laughter I'm feeling quite weak!'
(As trickles of merriment ran down his cheek.)
'My house-warming party I hope you won't spurn.
You must say you'll come and you'll give us a turn!'

At this, the poor spectre — quite out of his wits —
Proceeded to shake himself almost to bits.
He rattled his chains and he clattered his bones
And he filled the whole castle with mumbles and moans.

But Colonel Fazackerley, just as before,
Was simply delighted and called out, 'Encore!'
At which the ghost vanished, his efforts in vain,
And never was seen at the castle again.

'Oh dear, what a pity!' said Colonel Fazack.
'I don't know his name, so I can't call him back.'
And then with a smile that was hard to define,
Colonel Fazackerley went in to dine.

CHARLES CAUSLEY

Sir Nicketty Nox

Sir Nicketty Nox was an ancient knight,
So old was he that he'd lost his sight.
Blind as a mole, and slim as a fox,
And dry as a stick was Sir Nicketty Nox.

His sword and buckler were old and cracked,
So was his charger and that's a fact.
Thin as a rake from head to hocks,
Was this rickety nag of Sir Nicketty Nox.

A wife he had and daughters three,
And all were as old as old could be.
They mended the shirts and darned the socks
Of that old antiquity, Nicketty Nox.

Sir Nicketty Nox would fly in a rage
If anyone tried to guess his age.
He'd mouth and mutter and tear his locks,
This very pernickety Nicketty Nox.

HUGH CHESTERMAN

Sir Smasham Uppe

Good afternoon, Sir Smasham Uppe!
We're having tea: do take a cup.
Sugar and milk? Now let me see —
Two lumps, I think? . . . Good gracious me!
The silly thing slipped off your knee!
Pray don't apologise, old chap:
A very trivial mishap!
So clumsy of you? How absurd!
My dear Sir Smasham, not a word!
Now do sit down and have another,
And tell us all about your brother —
You know, the one who broke his head.
Is the poor fellow still in bed? —
A chair — allow me, sir! . . . Great Scott!
That *was* a nasty smash! Eh, what?
Oh, not at all: the chair was old —
Queen Anne, or so we have been told.
We've got at least a dozen more:
Just leave the pieces on the floor.
I want you to admire our view:
Come nearer to the window, do;
And look how beautiful . . . Tut, tut!
You didn't see that it was shut?
I hope you are not badly cut!
Nor hurt? A fortunate escape!
Amazing! Not a single scrape!
And now, if you have finished tea,
I fancy you might like to see
A little thing or two I've got.
That china plate? Yes, worth a lot:
A beauty too . . . Ah, there it goes!
I trust it didn't hurt your toes?
Your elbow brushed it off the shelf?
Of course: I've done the same myself.
And now, my dear Sir Smasham — Oh,
You surely don't intend to go?
You *must* be off? Well, come again.
So glad you're fond of porcelain!

E.V. RIEU

Bad Sir Brian Botany

Sir Brian had a battleaxe with great big knobs on;
He went among the villagers and blipped them on the head.
On Wednesday and on Saturday, but mostly on the latter day,
He called at all the cottages, and this is what he said:

'I am Sir Brian!' (ting-ling)
'I am Sir Brian!' (rat-tat)
'I am Sir Brian, as bold as a lion —
Take that! — and that! — and that!'

Sir Brian had a pair of boots with great big spurs on,
A fighting pair of which he was particularly fond.
On Tuesday and on Friday, just to make the street look tidy,
He'd collect the passing villagers and kick them in the pond.

'I am Sir Brian!' (sper-lash!)
'I am Sir Brian!' (sper-losh!)
'I am Sir Brian, as bold as a lion —
Is anyone else for a wash?'

Sir Brian woke one morning, and he couldn't find his battleaxe:
He walked into the village in his second pair of boots.
He had gone a hundred paces, when the street was full of faces.
And the villagers were round him with ironical salutes.

'You are Sir Brian? Indeed!
You are Sir Brian! Dear, dear!
You are Sir Brian, as bold as a lion?
Delighted to meet you here!'

Sir Brian went a journey, and he found a lot of duckweed:
 They pulled him out and dried him, and they blipped him on the head.
They took him by the breeches, and they hurled him into ditches,
 And they pushed him under waterfalls, and this is what they said:

'You are Sir Brian — don't laugh,
 You are Sir Brian — don't cry;
You are Sir Brian, as bold as a lion —
 Sir Brian, the lion, good-bye!'

Sir Brian struggled home again, and chopped up his battleaxe,
 Sir Brian took his fighting boots, and threw them in the fire.
He is quite a different person now he hasn't got his spurs on,
 And he goes about the village as B. Botany, Esquire.

'I am Sir Brian? Oh, no!
 I am Sir Brian? Who's he?
I haven't got any title, I'm Botany —
 Plain Mr. Botany (B).'

A.A. MILNE

Walter Spaggot

Walter Spaggot, strange old man,
Does things wrong-ways-round,
Like back-to-front or inside-out,
Or even upside-down.

He puffs his pipe inside his ear,
Has glasses for his mouth,
And if he wants to travel North
Walks backwards to the South.

He comes from whence he never is
And goes to where he's been,
He scrubs his shirt in the bath-tub
And baths in the washing-machine.

Walter Spaggot, strange old man,
Does things wrong-ways-round,
Like back-to-front or inside-out,
Or even upside-down.

(Funny old man.)

PETER WESLEY-SMITH

Herbaceous Plodd

Herbaceous Plodd
is rather odd.
His eyes are red,
his nose is blue,
his neck and head
are joined by glue.
He only dines
on unripe peas,
bacon rinds
and melted cheese.
He rarely talks,
he never smiles,
but goes for walks
with crocodiles.

MICHAEL DUGAN

The Folk Who Live in Backward Town

The folk who live in Backward Town
Are inside-out and upside-down
They wear their hats inside their heads
And go to sleep beneath their beds.
They only eat the apple peeling
And take their walks across the ceiling.

MARY ANN HOBERMAN

Elastic Jones

Elastic Jones had rubber bones.
He could bounce up and down like a ball.
When he was six, one of his tricks
Was jumping a ten-foot wall.

As the years went by, Elastic would try
To jump higher, and higher, and higher.
He amazed people by jumping a steeple,
Though he scratched his behind on the spire!

But, like many a star, he went too far,
Getting carried away with his power.
He boasted one day, 'Get out of my way,
I'm going to jump Blackpool Tower.'

He took off from near the end of the pier,
But he slipped and crashed into the top.
Amid cries and groans, Elastic Jones
Fell into the sea with a plop.

DEREK STUART

Listen, I'll Tell You . . .

Listen, I'll tell you
a wonderful thing:
there was an old woman
made wholly of string!

Her legs and her arms
and her pinafore, too,
her fingers and stockings,
the lace in each shoe —

and even her hair
which was longer than mine —
was made from a tenpenny
bundle of twine.

Now, do you not think it
delightful to sing
of this twisty old woman
made wholly of string?

JEAN KENWARD

Mr Nobody

I know a funny little man,
As quiet as a mouse,
Who does the mischief that is done
In everybody's house!
There's no one ever sees his face,
And yet we all agree
That every plate we break was cracked
By Mr Nobody.

It's he who always tears our books,
Who leaves the door ajar,
He pulls the buttons from our shirts,
And scatters pins afar;
That squeaking door will always squeak,
For, prithee, don't you see,
We leave the oiling to be done
By Mr Nobody.

He puts damp wood upon the fire,
That kettles cannot boil;
His are the feet that bring in mud
And all the carpets soil.
The papers always are mislaid,
Who had them last but he?
There's no one tosses them about
But Mr Nobody.

The finger-marks upon the door
By none of us are made;
We never leave the blinds unclosed,
To let the curtains fade.
The ink we never spill; the books
That lying round you see
Are not our books, they all belong
To Mr Nobody.

ANON.

Table Manners

The Goops they lick their fingers,
And the Goops they lick their knives;
They spill their broth on the table-cloth;
Oh, they live untidy lives.
The Goops they talk while eating,
And loud and fast they chew,
So that is why I am glad that I
Am not a Goop. Are you?

GELETT BURGESS

I Saw a Jolly Hunter

I saw a jolly hunter
  With a jolly gun
Walking in the country
  In the jolly sun.

In the jolly meadow
  Sat a jolly hare.
Saw the jolly hunter.
  Took jolly care.

Hunter jolly eager —
  Sight of jolly prey.
Forgot gun pointing
  Wrong jolly way.

Jolly hunter jolly head
  Over heels gone.
Jolly old safety-catch
  Not jolly on.

Bang went the jolly gun
  Hunter jolly dead.
Jolly hare got clean away.
  Jolly good, I said.

CHARLES CAUSLEY

Comedy

Many people make a living from making people laugh. Find out what you can about the lives of these comedians and what made them famous:

Buster Keaton
Charlie Chaplin
Peter Sellers
Morecambe and Wise
Laurel and Hardy
George Formby
Ken Dodd

Other Things To Do

1. Make a scrap-book of the jokes you know — try to include some of your own.
2. Choose one of the poems in this section and try to draw what you imagine the character looks like.
3. The 'Mr. Men' books by Roger Hargreaves have extraordinary characters in them. Try to write your own 'Mr. Men' book with illustrations.
4. Make a collage of drawings and paintings of your favourite cartoon characters.
5. Comedy is one of the most difficult forms of writing. Try to write your own funny play using everyday characters, but in a strange situation.